WILDERNESS EXPLORER

WILDERNESS EXPLORER

The Story of Samuel de Champlain

by CHARLES MORROW WILSON

ILLUSTRATED BY RICHARD LEWIS

Hawthorn Books, Inc.   Publishers

New York and London

H–9403

For Martha

AUTHOR'S NOTE

Samuel de Champlain was a master of many different skills, arts, and endowments. This fisherman's son who became the explorer, founder, and greatest colonizer of New France was a surprising number of things to a surprising number of people.

He was a seaman, a navigator, a geographer, and a cartographer or mapmaker, in each instance of outstanding ability. He also excelled as an artist with pen and brush and as a diplomat in the realms of government. Champlain was a way-shower for inland travel by rivers and lakes and an explorer who saw far beyond the immediately visible.

In faith, as in deeds and skills, this humble Frenchman from the almost forgotten sea port of Brouage was also a seeker after the stars and a master missionary. For good measure, Champlain was a great scholar who remains a constant challenge to lesser scholars.

In preparing this book, I have therefore, and with due humility, sought to pay maximum heed to my subject's own writings and interpretations. Both, fortunately, are quite extensive and, in all, cover about a third of Champlain's life.

My quest for incidental source materials has led to publications in earlier and contemporary French and Spanish as well as English. I am deeply indebted, too, to various publications and scholars of the Roman Catholic Church.

I am also greatly indebted to several local historical groups including the New Brunswick Historical Society, the Champlain Society of Quebec, the Geographical Society of Quebec and the Vermont Champlain Tercentennial Commission. In addition, I have consulted most of the biographies of Champlain. But I am most indebted to the splendid six-volume WORKS OF CHAMPLAIN as assembled, translated, and annotated by the pre-eminent Champlain Society with headquarters at Toronto.

CHARLES MORROW WILSON
Putney, Vermont.

THE CASE OF THE MISTAKEN PORTRAIT

Through the past century, schoolbooks, murals, and other paintings have represented Samuel de Champlain as large and quite plump, with a high forehead, large eyes, elegant dress, and a mustache and goatee in the style of Cardinal Richelieu. In this image, Champlain has repeatedly been pictured gazing heavenward, surrounded by adoring Indians.

The latter mentioned phases of the portrayal are in keeping with known facts. American Indians unquestionably adored Champlain. Otherwise, the long-used image simply does not dovetail with the known records. For example, we know that in real life Champlain was an explorer by land, sea, lake, and river. He repeatedly carried immense burdens for long distances. He survived ten official expeditions which included overland tramps of hundreds of miles; in one instance, his travels carried him more than a thousand miles.

We are reliably told, too, that Champlain ate moderately, sometimes from very limited food supplies. He survived many famines or near famines and frequently fasted. None of these responsible testimonies would indicate that he was fat, or even plump.

As for Champlain's dress, there are responsible testimonies that he was never a fop or dude. Even on trips to Paris or in the royal court of Henry IV or the latter's son, Louis XIII, Champlain is said to have dressed very inconspicuously, wearing the plain, dark apparel then standard to bourgeois or middle-class Frenchmen. In the field and throughout his career of official voyages, the great adventurer dressed, ate, and lodged as nearly as possible like his troops, crews, colonists, or Indian hosts. For these and many other reasons, Champlain scholars felt there was cause to doubt the authenticity of what had been regarded as his official portrait.

Back in 1904, Victor Hugo Paltsits, one of the most highly respected art historians of his time, succeeded in proving that the long-accepted "schoolbook portrait" of Champlain had been copied from a portrait painted originally by Moncornet who was a court portraitist for Louis XIV of France. This finding naturally aroused a contradiction in dates. The actual copy had been made in 1854, which was 219 years after Champlain's death in 1635. But the original, too, could not possibly have been painted during Champlain's lifetime. Moncornet's art career did not even begin until more than a dozen years after our subject's death.

During the 1930's, Dr. H. P. Bigger, who is regarded by many as the premier authority on Champlain, proved conclusively that the Moncornet portrait was not of Champlain at all, but rather of Louis XIV's short-time comptroller general, Michel Particelli.

C. W. Jaffreys, the artist who painted the famed mural of Champlain which you may now see in the Chateau Laurier in Ottawa, the capital of Canada, led the way in correcting the strange and ironic error of portraits. Supported by unchallengeable scholarship, artist Jaffreys pictures Champlain as medium tall, rather slender, definitely agile, black-haired, brown-eyed and dark-complexioned.

CONTENTS

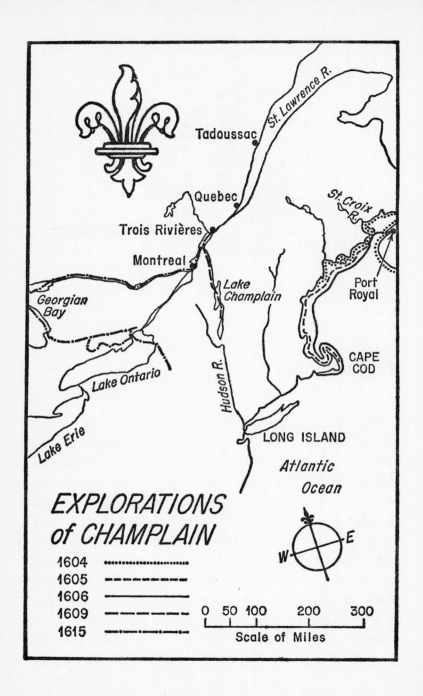

Tadoussac

St. Lawrence R.

Quebec

Trois Rivières

St. Croix R.

Montreal

Lake Champlain

Port Royal

Georgian Bay

Hudson R.

CAPE COD

Lake Ontario

Lake Erie

LONG ISLAND

Atlantic Ocean

N
W — E
S

EXPLORATIONS of CHAMPLAIN

1604 ....
1605 - - - - - -
1606 ————
1609 — — — —
1615 —·—·—·—

0 50 100   200   300
Scale of Miles

CHAPTER 1

A LOOK TO LAND

The fishing captain's son was slender, black-haired, dark-eyed and by averages of the time rather tall. At nineteen Samuel Champlain, only son of Antoine and Marguerite Le Roy Champlain, had reached his ultimate height of about five feet seven. Appropriately he was already on his way to learning his chosen trade, ship's navigator, and he was well on course with his native faith, Roman Catholic. In a sense this was entirely logical. At least throughout coastal Europe most fishing people of the times were Catholic, in the wake of the great founder, St. Peter.

Brouage, the home port of the Champlains and the

second largest seaport of all France, was vitally important to the great fishing fleets of Europe, from Scandinavia to what is now Italy. Located on the ancient Bay of Biscay in the province of Saintonge, some twenty miles south of La Rochelle and seventy miles north of Bordeaux, Brouage was the foremost salt "base" in all Europe. In those times salt for preserving the catches was the first essential of ocean fishing. Thousands and thousands of fishing vessels from a dozen nations regularly began "work voyages" by taking on ballasts of salt from the famed boiling flats of Brouage where shallow blockades of sea water were "sunned down" for salt or, as demand required, boiled down in great metal cones. The expanding Catholic world required fish for Friday and Lenten fare. Fishing required salt. Brouage supplied the salt.

The historic city provided some rather salty contradictions as well. Brouage was a famed Catholic port, yet it was also the ocean-edge capital for the new and aggressive wave of sixteenth century Protestantism. The Huguenots, as these Protestants were called, were named for France's first counterpart of John Calvin. By the time of the younger Champlain's birth on Christmas Day, 1567, the Huguenots were large in number, aggressive, devout, and strongly loyal to their land.

In some respects, and certainly throughout Champlain's early life, Brouage was the Cape Canaveral of its era. It was a takeoff point not for "outer space" but for the then unknown and unmarked outer earth, which included most of the continents and oceans. Samuel

Champlain was growing up just as the New World age came to flower.

Christopher Columbus, the most famous of the Genoese navigators, who had died only thirty-one years before young Champlain was born, unquestionably visited Brouage. There is evidence that the great Genoese navigator sailed from the salt port for his splendid but little-remembered Icelandic voyage. Almost certainly the Basque and Breton fishermen who discovered and plied the great fishing banks off Labrador and Newfoundland salted and sailed from Brouage long before 1492.

Thus young Champlain as a "home-porter"—he called it "Brouageasis"—had already viewed the start of historic journeys to many far and wondrous places. Sea life on fishing boats and land life in a stone cottage so near the sea that the greedy tides eventually destroyed it had been Samuel Champlain's very special school. Quite probably it was his only school.

In any case, Champlain described himself as "self-schooled." His journals, which filled many thousand revealing pages, proved beyond doubt that he was exceptionally well schooled. In a clear, warm style, and in the main without flourishes, he wrote plain but literate French. Except for an occasional lengthy sentence his journals are still excellent working models of good reporting.

For good measure he also painted well, mostly in water colors, and drew superbly. Hundreds of his line drawings of people, places, plants and animals of the

New World are still cherished by professional illustrators. A great many of his maps, including those of the Maritime Provinces of Canada and what is now the Maine coast, have served generations of mapmakers most helpfully. The northeast boundary between the United States and Canada is based directly on original maps made by Champlain two centuries before the boundary was finally established. His manuals and other writings of ship navigation are still quoted, respected and widely used.

Some scholars believe that Samuel learned the principles of navigation from his uncle, Pierre Champlain, who at one time was senior pilot for the Royal Spanish Navy. But there is very good evidence that Samuel learned seamanship on his own, beginning as a cabin boy aboard his father's fishing craft as a seven- or perhaps an eight-year-old. At nineteen he had already served at least ten years aboard ship.

Certainly Champlain knew a great deal about ships and their varied and distinguished hulls and riggings. He later wrote of the Portuguese carracks, the Flemish flyboats, the British hookers and roundbows, the French shallops and corsairs and the many other sailing ships which shaped and colored his childhood memories of his home port.

Young Samuel also knew a great deal about wars. Throughout his childhood and youth and, indeed, his early manhood, his beloved France and his city were being torn and trampled by many kinds of wars. Some were great wars between rising nations. Some were civil

Samuel learned seamanship on his own.

uprisings or fighting feuds between individual towns. And some were religious wars.

In 1589, after a restless interval of nine years of comparative peace, Samuel Champlain was watching his beloved home port suffer still another period of strife. The attackers this time were Huguenots. They represented only the rival seaport of La Rochelle and there was no special formality or war declaration involved. But the coastal neighbors were in deadly earnest. Though mustered locally, their attack force included several dozen fishing crafts and at least fifteen merchantmen, or cargo ships, all well-manned.

The defense of Brouage, such as it was, had been directed by the local governor, D'Epinay Saint-Lou, an ally of Henry of Navarre. At nineteen, Champlain was old enough to take part in the defense of Brouage and he did so. We are not sure in what capacity he served, but we do know that the attack took the form of a naval action, one of the most unusual ever recorded.

For an entire day the attacking fleet and the hometown "navy," made up mostly of fishing craft, bombarded one another with small deck cannon and rock-heaving catapults. It has been reported that there was not a single direct hit scored during the entire engagement. Quite evidently the sailors and sea fishermen did not excel as gunners. But when night came the attackers shifted to a strategy they knew. They climbed into small boats and under cover of darkness slipped into the harbor and proceeded to scuttle and sink the larger ships which waited at anchor. This left the smaller fishing boats completely unable to cope with the invasion force. So Brouage surrendered and La Rochelle was the victor in the strange war of rival ports.

Apparently resigned to the fact that Brouage, including its famed and coveted salt works, was doomed to unending strife, the Champlains looked to the sea for safety and peace. It is probable that in this looking the only child of the fishing captain and his good wife Marguerite already dreamed of the distant and vaguely known world beyond what was called the Western Ocean.

CHAPTER 2

"VOYAGE THE FIRST"

By 1594, the young man who had yearned for a life at sea found himself serving in northern France with the army of Henry of Navarre. From ship's navigator to army billeting officer, with a rank comparable to a sergeant major, he was to begin a long and illustrious military career.

There is no reason whatever for believing that Champlain ever enjoyed warfare. But at least, after 1594, when Henry of Navarre became Henry IV, King of France, the fighting was no longer province against province or town against town. Now, nation was fighting nation. France was in a life-or-death struggle with Spain, the most feared of all European powers.

At first it was a war of skirmishes, but in August of 1594, Marshal d'Aumont's prided force, in which Champlain served, led a great offense. Beginning at Rennes, D'Aumont's legion set out on the very same course which the American Sixth Armored Division was to follow exactly 350 years later in World War II.

D'Aumont was a stern soldier. Under his command, Champlain was required to enforce discipline and prevent looting. One tragic day when a group of twenty-eight French soldiers was placed under arrest for looting farm homes, Champlain decided the best course was to reprimand or "lecture" the culprits. His commanding officer, however, took him aside and told Champlain he was being too easy on the men and ordered all of the accused hanged. Deeply upset, Champlain formed a lifelong disapproval of capital punishment but along with it a very real respect for discipline.

When the Spanish army retreated to Brest and took refuge in the rocky point of Crozon, Champlain had the chance to prove that in terms of personal risks he was not lacking in courage. When the French force attacked, Champlain was at the forefront of his company. The offense was repeated a dozen times and French losses were heavy. Taking the last four hundred Spaniards cost the lives of more than three thousand Frenchmen. But the French army won decisively. Champlain survived and came out as one of the special heroes of the Crozon siege.

He won France's most coveted medal for valor. He also won the friendship of France's future king, as well as a "valor pension" of $2500 per year, and an open door to a career destined to make history and build nations across the Atlantic.

The war ended with victory for Navarre and the changing France he would rule. In May, 1598, King Henry came to Rennes and received his victorious troops. After five days of feasting, the French forces were paid, dismissed and left to shift for themselves.

At thirty-one, Samuel Champlain felt equal to the challenge. He had learned to lead others, to rely on himself, and, as he was shortly to prove, to keep one of the most revealing diaries ever written. In its earlier pages Champlain speaks of this period just after the war along lines known to many a war veteran: "Seeing myself without any charge or employment I resolved not to remain idle but to find some means for making a voyage to Spain. . . ."

Champlain bore no grudge against his military enemy. His plan, as he frankly stated it, was to get to Spain and seek work on one of the ships which the Spanish Crown sent each year to that part of the New World called the West Indies and Mexico. "And thus inform myself," he wrote, "of those facts which have not been learned by any Frenchman because they have no free access there; and so on my return I would make a truthful report of them to His Majesty. . . ."

He first tramped to Blauet on the south coast of Brittany. There he found quarters with Spanish troops for which the French had agreed to provide safe voyage back to their homeland. In Blauet, Champlain was also reunited with his Uncle Pierre, then employed by the King of Spain as pilot-general of the Spanish navy. Uncle Pierre welcomed his landlocked nephew and managed to find him a job as navigator aboard the *Sainte Julien*, a very large 500-ton fishing vessel which had been leased as a troop ship.

Whether or not Champlain had grown a bit rusty with compass, sextant and star reading, or whether his seaman's luck had run out we do not know. We do know that in August, 1598, while en route to Cádiz, the *Sainte Julien* ran into a ruinous Bay of Biscay storm. Champlain managed to ride her through to Vego Bay for repairs and refitting.

Setting forth from Vego he sailed into an even fiercer storm but again managed to reach harbor, this time at the mouth of the Seville River. However, the ship was severely damaged. Champlain expected to be court-martialed or discharged. He was, after all, an enlisted officer of the Spanish navy and as pilot he was fully responsible for the safety of the ship.

But the Spanish admiral, Don Francisco Coloma, was grateful to the young pilot for saving the ship and its men. The Admiral directed that the troops be dismissed and the craft be stanched and readied for a much farther voyage. He then commanded that Champlain remain aboard as a representative of the ship's owners who were Frenchmen.

By that time Champlain knew that the *Sainte Julien* had been chosen for the Spanish Crown's special journey to the West Indies and Mexico. Happily he joined in

"God pilots the pilot."

outfitting for the long voyage. "God," he wrote, "pilots the pilot."

Early in the following January, the passenger and cargo lists began arriving at the outfitting port of San-lucar de Barremeda. There were soldiers, including fourteen officers. There was a ship's company of some thirty Spaniards. There were royal cartographers or mapmakers, but to Champlain's delighted surprise, there were no other navigators. And to his very great interest there were two parties of priests aboard, one of Jesuits, the other of Dominicans.

Champlain had never met any member of either of the great Orders before. In his earlier life he had known only the local parish priests and the local monastic Order, the Recollects, or Barefoot Friars of Brouage. Now he was beginning a lifelong, ever-admiring acquaintance with the two great missionary Orders of the era.

It was a gay ship. Not even foul weather could dampen the splendid morale. Perhaps in some part by intuition and no doubt with the counsel of crew, the French-speaking navigator set a course first for the Canary Islands, then south by west to parallel sixteen, then west by expected trade winds to the wonderlands called the Spanish West Indies. It was a bold course, but, as Champlain suggested, angels hovered in both the mainsails and bowsprit.

At the New World island now called Guadeloupe where the ship anchored to take fresh water and tropical fruits, Champlain had his first look at Indians or, as he called them, the Brown Ones. They were soon to become his lifelong and foremost interest. His liking for the natives was instant, but his first notation of how the evidently friendly natives fled in terror on hearing the roar of a fowling piece prompted Samuel to note that "white man and brown were as hunter and quarry."

As the *Sainte Julien* proceeded to tour the Caribbean, Champlain continued to observe in wide-eyed wonder, but on the more practical side, to sketch and record the more promising harbor sites. At Margarita Island off the Venezuelan coast, he watched the native pearl divers and marveled at their skill and courage. At Puerto Rico, in the harbor of San Juan, he viewed with foreboding the first evidence of white man's wars in the rainbowed and otherwise idyllic tropical paradise. British ships had lately sacked the harbor and burned the settlement.

The Spanish ship headed for the coast of Mexico, then the foremost colony of Spain. At a point near Vera Cruz the Jesuits, Dominicans, and the ship's soldiers disembarked and set out on foot for the rugged overland journey to Mexico City. Champlain eagerly joined the expedition.

Day after day Champlain entered notes and sketches in his journal. The lowland jungles intrigued him. On arriving at Mexico City he could scarcely express his amazement. This remarkable highland capital already compared favorably with the capitals of Europe. As the sixteenth century was ending, it had a Spanish population of fifteen thousand and, as Champlain guessed, six times that number of Indians already converted to Christianity. On one page of his journal he noted his belief in the importance of "establishing the Christian Faith in the Wilds of America." On the same page he also stated his dissatisfaction regarding Spain's ways of attaining this. Champlain observed that the English concept of colonizing appeared to be to put the natives out of one's way, while the Spanish made the native a slave and put him to handing the white man the gold, silver, and other precious resources of this rich land.

Champlain disapproved of both policies. While as yet France had no important overseas empire, he hoped his own homeland would see fit to build one by joining the natives in "friendly alliance as equal factors to a common end."

He also had strong convictions about converting New World people to the Christian faith. After watching three very pretty Indian girls publicly whipped for failing to attend Mass and watching an elderly Indian man flogged to death for trying to escape from his place of forced employment, or better said enslavement, Champlain wrote: ". . . At the beginning of the King of Spain's conquests he had established the Inquisition among the Indians, and enslaved them, or caused them to die in such great numbers that the mere story of it rouses one's pity. This bad treatment was the reason that the poor Indians would flee to the mountains like desperate men. . . ."

In and between these lines and hundreds more like them one learns that almost instantly Champlain began liking the native Americans. He recognized their beauty, dignity and spiritual scope. As he clearly recorded, he saw them as "possessors of immortal souls which deserved to be won to God."

In some ways Champlain's reporting of what he termed his *Voyage the First* shows deep confusion regarding the character and purpose of his fellow men. In this land called Mexico with its tremendous beauty and stark terror, he had seen no fighting with swords or muskets. Yet he could not feel the sweet breath of peace, nor could he feel the strength of faith. The Spanish Empire was then the mightiest of all, but to Samuel Champlain the hallmark of this empire seemed more of gold than soul.

He granted that building empires requires goods which can be touched, held in the hands, eaten when one is hungry, or worn on the back when one is cold. However, Champlain spoke the hope and prayer that the New World empire of France would be built more for soul than gold, and that its yields should be of faith, timbers, crops, furs and the product which Samuel already knew a great deal about: fish.

CHAPTER **3**

THE NEW WORLD

Spain was rich enough and bold enough to seize colonies and make them properties of her Crown. The King-Emperor was owner. His henchmen, or royal appointees, managed the colonies with the purpose of delivering wealth to the royal treasury and greater power and glory to Spain and her monarchs. In return the Crown of Spain supplied the colonies with explorers, physicians, geographers, soldiers, seamen, military supplies, livestock, and even books and art objects.

But France was still neither strong nor wealthy enough to follow Spain's lead. Weak from generations of wars, both civil and foreign, France was, or at least felt, obliged to follow the examples of other powers such as England and Holland in its attempt to establish an overseas empire. The method was to found colonizing companies which were organized and financed for the profit of stockholders but with charters and bylaws approved or issued by the reigning monarch.

In return for the overseeing or ownership of lands or ports or other important resources and special advantages in valuable trading goods, the companies agreed to give services to the Crown. These services included paying money, providing ships, developing ports, building settlements and maintaining military forces or patrols. In this way, they frequently aided in changing poor countries into rich empires.

France began her ventures in the New World in 1584 when Champlain was seventeen. From Henry III, the Marquis de la Roche Helgomarch obtained a concession to occupy Newfoundland. The Marquis managed to recruit a hundred colonists in Brittany and stopped at Brouage to take on salt and fish. The westward journey proved disastrous. The ship was storm-wrecked off Nova Scotia. The survivors built a short-lived and tragically failing colony on Sable Island, a barren sand reef off Nova Scotia.

In 1600 Pierre Chauven, a Huguenot from Honfleur, scored the next failure. But at least the Huguenot fishing captain succeeded in reaching the Gaspé Peninsula and traveled south to establish a fur trading post and temporary colony at Tadoussac at the headwaters of the St. Lawrence.

The location was poorly selected and bitterly cold. The sixteen settlers who survived did so only because charitable Indians fed them. Chauven managed the following year to equip a rescue expedition to return the survivors to France.

Tadoussac had lasted as a fur trading base. But the number of furs received there was so small that the group of French seaport merchants who had financed the venture demanded that Chauven's trader's license be revoked. Henry IV, who was now King of France, complied and issued the license to Champlain's good friend the Governor and Vice Admiral Aymar de Chastes.

Promptly this leading citizen of Dieppe chartered three fishing boats and organized a fact-finding expedition. He made the aging but lusty Captain Pontgrave his senior shipmaster. Champlain, also with the rank of captain, went along as observer, mapmaker and, as the title would now be, executive officer.

For the quiet junior captain it was a great adventure; for the future of the French Empire it was only mildly noteworthy. On March 15, the expedition embarked from St. Malo in three small ships; the *Bonne Renommee*, the largest, on which Champlain served as navigator, was only 120 tons. Champlain could at least be thankful for the two young Montagnais Indians whom the company had procured as interpreters.

The voyage was stormy but well directed. On May 7, the voyagers sighted Newfoundland. After two weeks of maneuvering through ice floes they reached

The voyagers sighted Newfoundland.

Antiosti Island in the Gulf of Newfoundland. On May 27, Champlain first set foot on mainland Canada.

Along with many delightful drawings and descriptions of the wildlife of this region, Champlain's journals of his first adventures among the "brown men of the north" abounded in episodes:

"When the chieftain had ended his speech of welcome, we went out of his lodge where all the tribe waited to join us in the *tabajie* or feast. This they made with the flesh of moose, which is like beef, with that of bear, seal and beaver, which are their most ordinary meats and with great quantities of wild fowl.

"They had eight or ten kettles full of meat in the midst of the said lodge, and these were set some ten paces apart and each on its own fires. The men sat on both sides, each with his porringer (bowl) made of the bark of a tree, and when the meat is cooked, one of them apportions to every man his part. . . ."

The girls and young women, meanwhile, most of them beautifully figured and quite pretty of face, were having their turn of play. Their special "antic" was standing upright in fragile birchbark canoes in a nearby river, drifting past the men's feasting ground and performing a sort of willowy twist dance without upsetting the canoes. It was a feat requiring great skill and surprising grace.

But Champlain quickly noted some sombre undertones to the gaiety. "When they (the men) had ended their feast, they, too, began to dance, taking in their hands as a mark of rejoicing the scalps of their en-

33

emies. . . . They would stop sometimes and cry 'Ho, Ho, Ho' and again begin to dance. . . . They were celebrating for a victory they had won over the Iroquois of whom they had slain about a hundred. . . ."

As his days of camp visiting followed, Champlain observed that the Indians, gracious and appealing as they were, believed warfare to be part of their destinies. From repeated friendship visits to such typical nations as the Montagnais, who were the Algonquins of the lower St. Lawrence; the Elchemus or Penobscot Algonquins of what is now Maine; and presently the Algonquins proper who had headquarters on the Ottawa River, he learned that the mighty federation of northern Indians, including the Hurons to the northwest, were historic enemies of another mighty federation.

The latter was the Iroquois Confederacy of what is now upper New York State. The Iroquois, from all appearances, were almost professional warriors. They operated many farms, but also maintained armies numbering high into the thousands. For generations, well-led combat groups of Iroquois had been raiding and plundering the St. Lawrence homelands of the Algonquins. Now that the fur trade was beginning to grow, Iroquois raiding parties were regularly capturing great wealth in fine northern furs which were the special resource of the Algonquins.

As a peace-loving man who knew a great deal about warfare, Champlain's first impulse was to explore pos-

sibilities for encouraging peace between the two domi-
nant federations. From all he had heard, however, he
came to the conclusion that this was quite impossible.
Both federations believed they were born to fight each
other. France, therefore, was obliged to choose sides.
And if the hoped-for fur trade were to endure, the Algonquins as suppliers of the finer furs were the logical
allies of France.

Champlain noted thoughtfully: "The make of warfare which they (the Algonquins) practice is altogether
by surprises; for otherwise they would be afraid and
too much in dread of the said Iroquois who are in
greater numbers. . . ."

Champlain continued to ponder the basic problem.
Only by joining the Algonquins could France win the
fur trade. Yet, alas, only by joining the Iroquois could
New France include this great and perhaps someday
decisive land to the south.

Week after week, usually alone except for one interpreter and a friendly chief, Champlain made seem-
ingly endless rounds of visits to Indian settlements. He
learned to maneuver the amazing birchbark canoes
which easily carried half a ton of cargo yet were
light enough for one man to carry on his shoulder.
He slept and talked in the "summer wigwams" covered
with skins or tree bark.

From the very first day ashore in the New World
Champlain showed the viewpoint of a sincere and
fervent missionary. The Indians had no native religion,

at least no religion Champlain could recognize as such. His first plea was to teach the people Christianity. ". . . I think they would speedily be brought to be good Christians if their country were colonized. . . ."

On June 18, 1603, Champlain launched one of the most valiant journeys of exploration in American history. It was his now classic logging and mapping tour of the St. Lawrence Valley. He chose to travel light. He took only an interpreter, two oarsmen, and an Indian who was a petty chief and had ventured into some of the St. Lawrence tributaries. His boat was a pinnace, a kind of dory or utility boat which had been deck-stowed on the *Bonne Renommee.*

There was danger involved due to violent rapids, summer storms and possible ambush from Iroquois raiding parties. But Champlain appeared to disregard these completely. The first week's travel brought the slender craft to the Quebec Narrows.

The explorer became a farm reporter. He described the hillsides of wild grapes above the Ile de Orleans and the beautiful deep-soiled countryside fronting the Narrows. "The soil if tilled would be as good as in France," he noted. He stopped to taste and appraise the wild-growing crops including hazelnuts, wild grapes and cherries, and groundnuts or Indian potatoes.

At Three Rivers, a confluence at the head of the tide-water, the farm reporter quickly changed back to military reporter. Champlain located a superb fort site, then thoughtfully wrote out a strategy which was to endure for all his thirty-year career as leader and builder

Champlain sought information from the natives.

of New France: *Keep the peace if possible. If keeping peace is impossible, protect the allies of France.*

Though the upstream travel grew more and more difficult Champlain pushed on boldly into the upper lands of the Iroquois. There he heard of an inland lake which was later to bear his name and beyond it a river of destiny to be named the Hudson.

July found him making camp at the foot of what is now St. Joseph Street in Montreal. Next Champlain viewed and felt the appalling strength of the Lachine Rapids: "I never saw any torrent of water pour over with such force as this does. . . ."

As becomes any good reporter, the man whom Indians were renaming the "Friendly Brownskin White Brother" sought information from natives whom he regarded as responsible. From their testimonies he made entries dealing in turn with a great lake (Ontario); a tremendous waterfall (Niagara); a "freshwater ocean" (Lake Erie); and a still larger body of water (Lake Huron), "which no man had seen because it is so vast they will not venture to put out in the same. . . ."

On the bodies of the far-traveling Hurons, whom the Algonquins listed as "the good Iroquois" (though allies of the Algonquins, the Hurons had once belonged to the Iroquois federation), Champlain saw bracelets and other adornments made of copper and heard accounts of rich copper mines. As both an army and a navy man he recognized the value of copper. He resolved to locate the mines.

But there was other important work which had to be done before the summer was over. The most urgent assignment was to locate a suitable place for building France's first permanent colony in the New World.

The downstream return to the supply harbor, Tadoussac, took only ten days. Champlain recorded it as a beautiful trip through a dreamlike series of beautiful places. He did not seem to be even faintly concerned with danger. Actually, of course, there was great danger. A feeble little boat, manned by newly arrived white men, had traveled nearly a thousand miles upstream. On all sides were unknown natives. There had been fierce storms and floods. The inland rivers abounded in whirlpools and fierce rapids which roared like thunder and could crush people and boats like so many eggs dropped on stones.

But Champlain saw this almost unbelievable New World as a vast green paradise. The entire journey had been peaceful. As he eased his boat into Tadoussac, the log-built pier on the Gulf of St. Lawrence drowsed in summer sun and seemed to smile a welcome.

Then a birchbark canoe came darting to the bow of the pinnace boat. A young Indian, a Montagnais Algonquin, began speaking to Champlain in the musical language of his people. Unable to understand the pleasant singsong which sounded as if it were made up of vowels without any consonants at all, Champlain turned to his interpreter who began to translate:

"The brave is telling you that a great battle has been

fought on waters we have just traveled. It was a canoe battle between our Algonquin friends and the Iroquois. It was a victory for the brave Algonquins."

Champlain found himself almost unable to believe that the waterway journey of peace could have come within a stone's throw of a fierce battle. He did not understand how battles could be waged from canoes. But most of all, he wondered what had caused this battle between the two tribes.

When he questioned the interpreter, the Indian replied, "There is always cause for battle between the Algonquins and the terrible Iroquois. We were born to fight each other. They, the wicked ones, would rob us of our furs and our wives and children. And our homes, hunting lands and fishing waters would be ruined by these invading thieves."

Champlain's next question also brought a ready answer: "For brave warriors, canoes are very good to fight from. Our paddlers can sweep close to the enemy while our strong bowmen pierce him with arrows."

"What happens when you—we, that is—run out of arrows?"

"When that happens, we turn over our canoes and swim to shore underwater."

Champlain listened unhappily. "Not all of us," he pointed out. "I can't swim—even when my head is above water."

The two ships which the new colonizing and fur

trading company operated were anchored at Tadoussac ready to sail for France. Plans had been made for returning the following spring to set up a permanent French colony somewhere in the area. Champlain would go to Paris to complete his maps and charts and to report to the King.

Before their departure, however, Champlain asked permission to take one of the sailing ships and make a short trip along the coasts of what are now the Maritime Provinces of Canada. He wished to see more of the possible sites for the proposed colony. He also wished to make a more complete report on the far-stretching coastline.

Captains Pontgrave and Preveit, who commanded the ships, agreed. Champlain took over the larger ship and its crew. Captain Pontgrave's ship took on the rest of the force and headed back to France.

With good crewmen helping, Champlain explored and mapped five different coastal sites which seemed worth considering as places for building colonies. He also wrote a careful report on the progress and promise of the fur trade. Champlain was quite certain that fine northern furs would be the surest source of wealth for New France.

Once more Champlain took time to visit with the Indians. The coastal tribes were quite cordial. Many asked him to take them along for his journey to France and, of course, to bring them home again. He felt that it would be quite worthwhile to let his king and other

Parisians see at first hand these people of the New World. After a great deal of thought, Champlain decided to invite an Indian mother and child to return with the force to Paris. He selected from the many who wished to go a pretty young princess, wife of a Montagnais chief, and her six-year-old son.

In almost ideal weather, the homebound trip was completed in eighteen days. That was something of a record for those times, and spoke well of Champlain's skill as a navigator. But "Sieur Samuel" began to feel concerned about how his guests would fare in Paris and how he could best succeed in interesting the homeland people in the wonderland that was New France.

On arriving in Paris the run of good fortune seemed to have ended. The first head of the company which had been founded to build up the France beyond the Western Ocean had recently died. The King and Council seemed undecided about the next step. While minds were being made up, Champlain introduced his Indian guests to the King and the staff of Louvre Palace. The Indian woman, who was Iroquois born and named "One of Beauty," abruptly grew ill and a few weeks later died.

Following this, the little boy was adopted by the royal court, baptized, dressed in a handsome blue cloak and bonnet, and lodged in the royal palace of Saint Germain. Dauphin Louis, then the three-year-old crown prince of France, was delighted with his new playmate from the western land. He had his young

Indian friend showered, or, as Champlain said, rained under, with his favorite foods—rich soups, tarts, candies, jellies and other confections. At first the little Indian gorged happily, then nibbled sadly, and then after eight months of the too rich fare, grew very ill and died.

Politely, but determinedly, Champlain sought his King's ear:

"Sire," he pointed out, "these Frenchmen of the New World cannot be treated like Old World Frenchmen. They must eat, sleep and live in their own ways, which are very different from ours."

King Henry IV was very interested in hearing more about this land and its people that held such promising expansion for France. He commanded Champlain, as his official geographer for the expedition, to provide him with all the information gathered from Champlain's explorations.

Champlain complied. He urged again the need for permanent colonies of Frenchmen to defend and help the Indians help themselves to better lives. He quickly completed and handed in his journals, drawings, maps and charts he had recently made in New France.

With the King's permission he then compiled and published a volume of the reports. The book was entitled *Des Sauvages, Voyage de Samuel Champlain de Brouage*. He dedicated the book to Charles de Montmorency, Admiral of the French Navy. The book quickly became a best seller.

Meanwhile "Voyager Samuel Champlain de Brouage" had time to think over his newly found fame and good fortune. At barely thirty-six he was already a successful author, a welcomed though yet untitled member of the King's court, a royal pensioner, a proud holder of his country's most honored medal for bravery, and, besides all that, a fairly contented bachelor. He was not bound to any future service to his country.

Who could ask for anything more?

Samuel Champlain could and did. He asked for a chance to help build New France as a great overseas empire and a new stronghold for the Catholic faith.

CHAPTER 4

VOYAGE OF HOPE

Again fortune seemed to smile on Champlain. Late
in October, 1603, the King's Council appointed a good
friend and former army comrade of Champlain as
new head of the Company of New France (it was later
renamed the Company of the One Hundred Associates). He was Pierre du Gua, the sieur C. de Monts,
who was also Vice Admiral of the Navy and Lieutenant General of the Army of France. Interestingly,
Admiral-General de Monts found himself appointed
Royal Commander of all of what is now called North
America from forty degrees north latitude, approxi-
mately on line with Philadelphia to Cape Breton. The

45

colonizing company would hold all rights to the fur trade for a period of ten years.

In return, de Monts and followers agreed "to establish the name, power, and authority of the King of France throughout the new territory . . . and summons the natives to the knowledge of the Christian religion." They were also commanded to "make peace with the native princes and their people; cultivate and settle the said lands; make explorations and especially seek out mines of precious metals. . . ."

Kings' decrees were usually full of flowery language. This directive was very forthright and to the point. One who studies the original documents feels that just possibly Champlain had a direct hand in the writing of this decree.

De Monts accepted the charge and promptly offered Champlain the post of geographer and mapmaker. At almost the same time, Champlain received directly from the King a commission as Captain of the Royal Navy and Royal Geographer for New France.

De Monts and Champlain began a search for suitable colonists. The first volunteer was Jean de Biencourt, an old soldier who wished establishment as "lord of the wilderness." De Monts liked old soldiers who, like himself, were not too old to dream and dare. He also saw the need of tradesmen and young soldiers. He employed a total of seventy artisans, mostly carpenters and masons, and forty soldiers, all Swiss hirelings. Champlain requested that a priest be taken along. De Monts, a fervent Huguenot, refused. They argued, then settled by taking along a priest, Father Aubrey of Rouen.

By gradual stages the company's stockholders began to advance the necessary money. From St. Malo, La Rochelle, Rouen, St. Jean de Luz and other ports, the town traders, ship owners, and merchants began buying shares in the company which was authorized to engage as its directors saw fit in fishing, lumbering, and mining, as well as fur trading.

Having again chartered the *Bonne Renommee* and another 150-tonner, the *Timothu* of Le Havre, De Monts completed the recruiting and supplying. The two ships set sail from Le Havre on March 7, 1804, Nova Scotia bound.

It was a stormy voyage. Champlain was concerned about the choice of colonists. Commander de Monts shared this concern. Some had been picked simply because there had been no better prospects.

"We have six pigs and six sheep aboard," Champlain noted. "I'm beginning to think they're our best behaved passengers except, of course, our priest and ourselves."

Commander de Monts seemed to ignore the quip. "We would do best to direct course south of the fishing banks. Do you know a sheltered bay where we could make a temporary camp?"

Champlain suggested that they set course for Halifax and veer south to the bay which he had named Point Moulton.

"You're the navigator," the Commander said curtly.

Champlain had barely returned to the chart room when the *Timothu* began pounding into the worst storm yet encountered. It continued through two fearsome days. There were no serious injuries, but there were indications that some of the passengers might not survive.

"Nothing brings out the true nature of people like a stormy voyage," Champlain told his commander.

De Monts nodded. "Appears as if our so-called soldiers and other landlubbers are already sorry they signed on. I gather our carpenters and masons are crying for the cafés and quoit rooms back in their hometowns." The older man sighed, then added, "But I will say that as pilot you're setting a good example."

"That's the pilot's job," Champlain answered.

"Since we have a soft passenger list it will be your job, too, to pick a soft place to land all these soft people," the Commander said.

On quieting seas Champlain rechecked course and brought the ship safely into Point Moulton. There the colonists went dashing ashore like happy children on a picnic. They began raising brush shelters, fishing, and netting the swarming native rabbits. Champlain took time to locate a plot for building pens for the livestock. He led a work force which felled small trees and with them built rail fences to enclose the six pigs and the six sheep, New France's first domesticated animals.

"This place will be all right for a summer camp," De

Monts said, "but we must look over the other sites you mentioned. Should we sail one of the ships down coast?"

"I recommend that you let me pick a small crew and try it in the pinnace," Champlain answered.

"A good suggestion," the Commander agreed, "but as a first move I'd prefer to leave the colonists here and sail our master ship down coast. I have a feeling we'll find some fellow Frenchmen buying furs without license. We have to keep an eye on those poachers."

"You're the commander," Champlain said.

De Monts laughed. "And you're the geographer. You can take the pinnace for that work. I'll take the mother ship as far as what you call St. Mary's Bay. You can have the pick of ship's company, including," the Commander added, "that seasick priest you insisted on bringing along."

"Father Aubrey's doing all right now," Champlain pointed out. "He's a brave spirit. He tells me he prefers to stay on as ship's chaplain—at least until he finds his sea legs."

"Very well, Captain. I'm a Protestant Huguenot, but not too prejudiced to take along a Catholic priest who wishes to go."

Having discharged most of the supplies, Commander de Monts ordered sails set for St. Mary's Bay. Father Aubrey, who had suffered from weeks of extreme seasickness, found himself feeling better.

When the ship lowered anchor, he asked to go ashore

for a stroll in the beautiful sunshine of the strange and alluring green shoreline. But the village priest from the district of Vincennes had no experience in finding his way through this roadless and pathless wilderness. He soon lost sight of the ship and all sense of direction.

Later in the day the Commander sent a search party to find the missing pastor. The searchers returned without success. They feared the priest had been kidnapped or killed by natives.

"We'll make another try at finding our blackrobe! And I will personally lead this search party," De Monts said.

But within the hour he noticed that a storm was brewing to the northeast. He realized that his ship was poorly placed for fronting it. So the Commander returned to the beach where he ordered a chorus of trumpet blows, then the firing of the ship's cannon, in hope that the priest would hear the uproar and be led back to the ship. There was no answer except the whine of the approaching storm and the roughening sea. De Monts gave orders to lift anchor in order to protect the ship.

Back at Point Moulton, meanwhile, Champlain had made sure that the new colonists were sheltered and supplied and set out on his own shoreline exploration. He rigged out the smaller pinnace boat and with only an Indian guide as companion he braved the now stormy coastline. His first goal was to locate the copper mines about which many Indian friends had told him. By lucky happenstance he headed first for St. Mary's Bay, though, of course, he had not heard of the sad plight of his friend, Father Aubrey.

Having beached and tied up his little boat, Champlain and his Indian guide set out inland. They had walked only a couple of miles when Champlain thought he heard a voice. After a moment of intense listening he was quite certain he did. With his guide trotting behind, the explorer hurried to locate the sound. At the head of a dense ravine he heard a prayer being spoken in French.

Hurriedly, Champlain began searching among the densely growing trees. Very soon he saw a blackrobed figure kneeling on a grassy mound. Hardly able to believe his eyes, Champlain ran to the priest's side and lifted him into his arms.

Father Aubrey was too feeble to stand alone. He had gone without food for nearly three weeks. As the rescuer lifted him into his strong arms, the famished priest said, "God has sent you here—a worthy servant in answer to the prayers of an unworthy servant."

"I am the most favored by God," Champlain answered. "I am his unworthy servant who has been permitted to save his most worthy servant."

The priest was weeping. "I cannot agree with what you say, my son. But I will join you in giving thanks to Him in whose sight we will both henceforth be more worthy."

51

The Indian waited in wondering silence while the two knelt together to give thanks. Then, with great gentleness, Champlain carried Father Aubrey back to the waiting pinnace. The good priest was briar-scratched and shrunken from his long ordeal. Champlain made him a porridge of salted fish, then after searching a nearby grove he came back with a cap full of what he called "winter fruits"—wild-growing chestnuts which were probably chinquepins. Then, carefully, he placed the exhausted and starved man in the pinnace and covered him with the blankets he had brought for his own use. After making sure that Father Aubrey was as comfortable as possible in the cramped quarters, he set sail hoping that with the added power of the oars they would locate the supply ship with all speed.

Having some knowledge of the territory, Champlain took a chance on finding Commander de Monts in what is now the Annapolis Basin. Once more his instinct had proved right. Upon entering the sheltered body of water their hearts lifted to see the ship that would provide food and rest for Father Aubrey.

Commander de Monts welcomed his aide and for the first time had a kind word for Father Aubrey. But he pointed out quite emphatically that it was now late in June and high time to be selecting a site for the permanent colony. The delay caused by the loss of the priest had cost them three weeks and the Commander knew they had much work to do before they would be able to face the winter months ahead.

With Champlain in agreement, he ordered the supply ship headed southwest along the New Brunswick coast. On St. John's Day, June 24, the ship's company located a good harbor at the mouth of a broad deep river. Commander de Monts named the place St. John and it has since become the provincial capital of New Brunswick.

De Monts, however, decided to push on southward, to sail on into Passamaquoddy Bay and head into the St. Croix River. A short way upstream the voyagers came upon a little island some five acres in area. A landing party found the soil fertile, trees plentiful for building log houses, and clay suitable for making brick.

Champlain reported: "This place (St. Croix Island) we considered the best we had seen both on account of its situation, the fine country and for the intercourse we were expecting with the Indians of the coast and of the Interior. . . . In the course of time we hoped to pacify them, and put an end to the wars they wage against one another . . . and convert them to the Catholic faith. . . ."

Champlain was ordered to take the pinnace back to Point Moulton and return on the *Timothu* with the colonists and supplies. This job was completed with speed and efficiency for Champlain was anxious to begin the farming venture that he hoped would provide the much needed food for the community.

After arriving in their new home, Champlain located and assigned each man a garden plot and distributed the available seeds which included peas, rye, beans, and

53

parsnips. But the planting was late and the season dry. Their first New World crops were disappointing. So was the progress of the colony. On the last day of August, De Monts ordered the two ships back to France and left Champlain in command of the skeleton crew that was to remain on the island.

With only two pinnaces for transportation, he rigged the larger one, an 18-tonner with a lateen sail, and made ready to explore and map the southward coasts. He had kept a force of twelve sailors to form the ship's company and these served him as oarsmen. Also helping were two friendly Indians who went along as interpreters and ambassadors.

So outfitted, Champlain set forth on his third voyage of discovery. His beautifully drawn maps, which are actually superior to many Maine coast maps now in use, record his progress.

They explored the shore lines of Penobscot and Casco Bays, then pressed through a "mull of fog" to circle the well-wooded island named Mount Desert. At that point the pinnace crashed against a high boulder hidden by the heavy weather. Cold water began gushing into the stern of the narrow wooden boat. Hastily, Champlain reset the foresail and joined his helpers in manning the oars. Working together, they managed to land the sinking craft.

Again this amazingly able man showed another phase of his ever-varied talents. He grabbed up a broadheaded ax and felled a large oak tree. Then he chopped the trunk into yard-long pieces and split these into thick boards which he shaped into mending timbers. Having plugged the holes in the stern and portside of the pinnace, he proceeded to "bleed" some pine trees, using the gum sap or turpentine as calking. While the repairs were drying, Champlain directed his Algonquin interpreter and guide to go inland and invite any Indians he met to come down for a parley.

Shyly, at first in small groups, the island Indians began to appear. Champlain waved greetings and began handing gifts to each comer. At first he gave jackknives. As larger groups appeared he began giving out hatchets and rosaries.

The Indians understood the use and value of the knives and hatchets, but the rosary beads bewildered them. "Tell our friends," Champlain instructed his interpreter, "that those bead strings are the most precious of all the gifts. And that in time they will find out why that is true."

Having proved that the pinnace was once again seaworthy, the party pressed on past Deer Island. Champlain next steered into the mouth of the Penobscot River. Finding the passageway blocked with great boulders, he beached the boat and walked upshore to the great falls and salmon pools. As he headed back to the shore he was startled to see a fleet of some twenty Indian canoes sweeping downriver toward him.

Champlain raised his arms in the gesture of peace and called back to his Algonquin interpreter, "Tell these people we are friends. Find out who their sagamore (great chief) is and ask him to land and join me."

A few moments later one of the birchbark canoes sped into the shallows. A tall Indian whose beaded tunic and necklaces of animal teeth indicated chief's rank strode toward the man who waited on shore. He was the great Bessabez, sagamore of the Sourequise, a coastal tribe related to the Algonquins.

Champlain greeted the sagamore and gestured welcome to the braves who were now swarming the shore. After a hurried conversation between the interpreter and Chief Bessabez, the Algonquin said, "Bessabez fears too much delay. His pursuers are another tribe of coast people led by a sagamore named Calabez. When last seen his canoe fleet was headed for the river's mouth.

"He says a war is being made against him," the interpreter continued. "He is seeking a proper place to make battle. The enemy is already about to overtake him and his warriors."

Quickly, Champlain led the way to the waiting pinnace and from its forehatch lifted out a bag full of shiny new hatchets. He turned to his interpreter. "Borrow a canoe and take this bag upriver. Find Calabez. Give him and his warriors these presents and ask them to wait in the shallows until I can join them."

When the Montagnais obeyed, Champlain called for his other Algonquin companion: "Tell the great chief here that if he and his people will be our friends; we will try to make peace for him with his enemies."

Sagamore Bessabez listened thoughtfully, then nodded. Champlain gave more gifts, including sea biscuits which the Indians especially liked. Leaving his followers to serve as hosts, the peacemaker set out upstream. He walked hurriedly along the overhanging banks and presently reached the attacking party which, as he had hoped, had beached their canoes in preparation for a parley.

Having located Sagamore Calabez, Champlain resumed the giving of friendship tokens. "I also made them presents of hatchets, rosaries, caps, knives and other trinkets, and . . . besides that I bartered with them for a small number of beaver skins," the explorer wrote.

That incident was a first and highly successful proof of the formula for mixing giving with trading and seeking a bonus in peace. The war party soon ceased being warlike. The great chief Calabez said he and his people didn't really want war; it was being forced on him.

With great deftness Champlain persuaded Calabez to take his canoe fleet home. Then he returned to his own party, assured the Sourequois group they had nothing further to fear, and set out to finish mapping another three hundred miles of coastline.

Not once did he complain about the fact that his party traveled unarmed, in a leaky little boat, in an unknown land of fierce Indian wars. He seemed to have

57

"I bartered with them for a small number of skins."

a mysterious gift for bringing peace to the savages on the warpath for in instance after instance local but long-lingering feuds among the native tribes were finally ended. France's friendship with the Maine and Canadian Indians, then being established by Champlain, was to endure through the centuries.

A canoe escort of Indians accompanied the explorer as far as Rockland Harbor. Champlain pushed on down the coast until an early October snow reminded him it was time to get back to prepare for the cold months ahead.

CHAPTER 5

STRUGGLE TO LIVE

Returned to St. Croix Island, he found himself face to face with the least reasonable of New World chieftains—King Winter.

Snow piled knee-deep. Bitter cold north winds came screaming through the mountain gaps. The little island, by then virtually cleared of trees, could not supply firewood. The shallow waters about it changed to barricades of ice blocks some twenty feet in the air. The island was thereby shut off from the mainland. Even the wine kegs froze solid. The harvested vegetables froze and salt meat had to be cut with saw and ax.

To make matters much worse, a plague of scurvy struck. Champlain, wiry, muscle-hard and healthy, found himself changed to head nurse and physician. He wrote out the unhappy facts:

"Their teeth became loose and fell out. . . . They were taken with great pains in the arms and legs . . . and they could not walk on account of the contracting of the nerves; consequently they had almost no strength and suffered intolerable pains. . . . The majority of the sick could neither get up nor move, nor could they be held upright without fainting away. . . ."

A total of seventy-nine men had volunteered to venture against a New World winter. Before the first April thaws began, thirty-five were dead of scurvy or related diseases. Twenty more were still too feeble to walk. Only eleven, including Champlain, remained well.

When the great barricades of ice finally broke, friendly Indians appeared with gifts of dried berries, nuts, and hard-to-get game. Champlain received the offerings thankfully but insisted on repaying in knives and rosary necklaces. He noted tersely that the tragic winter was more the result of man's fallibility than of God's will. He also stated that "proper foods," including fresh meats, tender herbs of springtime, and lemon or lime juice, are the best defenses against scurvy.

That was sound advice. And despite its suffering and tragedies the story of St. Croix colony is one of important history. It was, indeed, the first year-round white man's colony in America north of the Carolinas. It demonstrated the life-or-death need for subsistence farming and an accurate choice of colony sites.

On the more constructive and personal side, St. Croix

saw Champlain developing as an able leader of colonies, as well as of expeditions. He had not actually chosen the site, but he had survived and learned from its mistakes. Meanwhile, his mapping of the area is still of all-time excellence. Some two hundred years later, when the northeast boundary of the United States and Canada was finally confirmed by the Ashburton Treaty, the maps used were Champlain's originals!

Plans had been made for Captain Pontgrave to return to St. Croix in April, bringing a cargo of supplies and recruits. April dragged its hard, freezing course and no ship came. In May, sickness flared again. One of the victims was Father Aubrey. Champlain personally attended the priest and unashamedly wept while readying the service of final unction. But Father Aubrey did not die. He lingered near death for several weeks and then recovered.

As soon as Father Aubrey was well enough to make decisions, Champlain spoke to him of their desperate situation.

"I know, Father, that Captain Pontgrave promised to return for us in the spring, but I fear we will not last much longer if we do not get help soon."

"What would you plan to do, my son?" Father Aubrey asked. "I am too weak to be of any service to you, except that I'm not too weak to pray for our deliverance."

"We need your prayers always, Father, but I also

need your advice. I have been thinking that perhaps we should leave this place of death and starvation. Even the food our good Indian friends bring us will not feed so many hungry people."

Long into the night the priest and the adventurer talked of ways in which to save the remaining colonists from extinction. Father Aubrey convinced Champlain to wait just a little longer for Captain Pontgrave before he carried out the plan that he had formulated that night.

When June came, Champlain decided he could wait no longer and resolved to load the survivors in the two little boats and head for the Gulf of St. Lawrence in hope of being rescued by fishing ships.

The problems presented by this move were many and the risks great. Champlain still hesitated to put his people through what he knew would be a grueling experience. He also knew, however, that the alternative would be even worse: slow starvation and wretched disease.

On June 15, he had gathered the strongest of the men on shore to prepare the boats for sea. It was a discouraging business because the equipment as well as the people had suffered from the brutal winter.

Champlain could feel the resentment of the colonists. They felt it was safer to stay on the island and face known perils rather than put to sea in leaky boats and face unknown dangers. He had overheard one of the troublemakers of the group talking to his friends.

"He's going to kill us for sure! It was bad enough

being left behind when the Captain took the ships home. Now he wants us to leave just when the Captain is coming back. Why doesn't he wait, that's what I'd like to know!"

"But you weren't left here, Pierre. You volunteered like the rest of us," one of the party answered. "I think we ought to go along with our leader. Almost anything would be better than this. . . ."

Now Champlain stood looking out to sea, hearing the conversation in his memory. As he thought about the risks he was asking his people to take, he remembered the words of Father Aubrey. ". . . I'm not too weak to pray. . . ." This comforting phrase came almost at the same instant that he saw a sail far out on the ocean. Was it a mirage? Was it only because this was a sight he had been dreaming of for months? No! It was a sail! A tiny blotch of white on the blue sky. A shout burst from his lips and tears stung his eyes as he ran to tell the others the good news.

It was Captain Pontgrave's shallop. The company's other vessel, the *Saint Estienne*, was en route from St. Malo with supplies and replacements. Commander de Monts had authorized choosing a better colony site.

Champlain waited for the *Saint Estienne's* arrival, then made ready to resume exploring and mapping the New England coast. He directed repair and rigging of the larger pinnace and crewed it with twenty sailors, three newly arrived "gentlemen adventurers," two fellow pilots, Champdore and Cramolet, and an Indian couple, Chief Panounias and his wife.

One can only marvel how twenty-eight people managed in so small a boat. But they did, and Champlain launched a model example of a surveying journey.

He sailed into Casco Bay, where Portland, Maine, now stands, then passed Cape Elizabeth and Ram and Richmond Islands, where great reception parties of Indians waited. Having mapped what is now Old Orchard Beach, he sailed up the placid Saco River where Indians waved and danced on shore. These were handsome people, farming tribes who lived in log houses and cultivated fields of bush beans, corn, tobacco, pumpkins and other squashes, and grape vines.

Early in July, the expedition explored the sites of Kennebunkport and Cape Porpoise. Inland, Champlain viewed vast clouds of passenger pigeons and red-winged blackbirds.

East from Rockport he and his party saw young Indians who were dancing a sort of ballet, evidently for the onlookers' benefit. Champlain went ashore and gave each a knife and a sea biscuit—"which caused them to dance even better than ever. . . . When that was over I made them understand . . . that they should show me how the coast trended. After I had drawn for them with a charcoal the bay and island cape where we were, they pictured for me with the same charcoal another bay which they represented as very large. . . . Here they placed six pebbles at intervals . . . representing that number of chiefs and tribes. . . ."

What was "represented" was Massachusetts Bay and the six clans of Massachusetts Indians. The pinnace

He sailed up the placid Saco River.

pushed on past large Indian settlements where "fires of welcome" burned and into what is now Boston Harbor. Here Champlain again went ashore to receive welcomes and hand out knives, biscuits, and rosaries. He viewed with admiration the corn fields, the log houses, the dugout canoes made of tree trunks, and the beautiful Charles River.

Indians brought the voyagers gifts of sweet corn cakes and small squashes. Champlain described the squashes: ". . . as big as your fist which we ate as a saladlike cucumber, and they were very good. . . ."

On Plymouth Bay the voyagers visited Indian fishermen who received them like long lost brothers. In his journal of the journey, Champlain noted another way to the Indians' good will which he used quite effectively. This was music. In those times one of the most popular of musical instruments was the lap harp or zither. One of Champlain's younger followers had brought along his zither. The plaintive string music delighted the Indians.

In turn many things about the Indians delighted Champlain. He warmed to their friendship. He admired their farms and their beautifully tilled fields of corn and beans and artichokes. He shuddered sometimes at their ideas of beautifying themselves. Some of the coastal people painted their faces with great stripes of red, yellow, and black. Others blackened their faces like the cast of a minstrel show.

Another matter required more instant notice, however. One of the many problems related to coastal travel in a small boat with twenty-eight people aboard was keeping a supply of drinking water.

On a pleasant afternoon, Champlain landed the boat on a stretch of coastline and directed four of his sailors to take out the "kettles" or water kegs and fill them at a nearby fresh-water spring.

As the sailors neared the spring a band of Indians came out of a nearby forest. As usual, Champlain raised his arms in a salute of friendship. These Indians did not appear to notice. One of them made a dash toward the nearest sailor, grasped his water keg, and ran with it.

The surprised sailor gave chase. At that instant, more Indians came out of hiding with bows ready set with arrows. Champlain saw his sailor fall with many arrow shafts protruding from his body. Before he could leap from the pinnace other Indians ran to the scene and began to stab the fallen man.

Shouting to the other sailors to get back to the boat, Champlain pulled a musket from the storage hatch and raised it to fire a warning shot to frighten the marauding Indians. When he snapped the flintpiece the musket exploded. Fragments of metal glazed his head and cheeks and cut into his right hand. "Nearly killed me," the leader later casually noted.

In his dazed state he did not see that the three sailors who had escaped were back at the boat reaching for other muskets. With a swift movement, one of the men raised a weapon to his shoulder and aimed at the nearest savage.

Becoming aware of what his men were doing at last,

Champlain swung his arm up toward the barrel of the musket just as the sailor squeezed the trigger. The shot went wild and hit a tree not too far from where the Indians stood.

"We will fire only warning shots," Champlain snapped. "I will not allow you to kill the Indians. We have made peace with all the tribes we have met so far. We will not endanger that peace."

"Those savages killed our friend," one sailor shouted.

"We'll teach them a lesson!" another said. "We've got enough men and guns to fight a battle."

Champlain spoke very firmly. "There will be no battle. Put down the firearms!"

The sailors did not conceal their surprise and anger. "We've got to protect ourselves. Those copperheads killed our friend and comrade. We have to avenge Jacques."

Champlain by now was standing between the sailors and the supply of muskets or "thunder sticks."

"I agree that avenging is within our power," he said. "But it is not our right. . . . Vengeance is for God, not men."

"We must teach those savages a lesson," one of the men insisted.

"We can never teach the guilty by slaughtering those who may be innocent," Champlain replied.

Then he called for volunteers to help him bury the sailor remembered only as Jacques.

Without further mishaps the expedition pushed on to the coastline of what is now Rhode Island. There they met heavy fogs which told of latening summer. With regrets, the King's geographer decided to turn about and head back to the colony site. It was important for all the company to join in making ready for the long winter which would soon be overtaking them.

De Monts waited at St. Croix Island with a company-leased ship. He had delivered forty-five new colonists who had volunteered to serve one year in the New World. Most of those who had lived through their first year on the cold little island were more than eager to return to France. De Monts asked which of the group who had served out a year would be willing to stay on.

Only four of the group expressed such willingness. These were, Sieur de Fourgeray; Pilot Champdore; Father Aubrey, who was still tottery and weak after his long illness during the previous winter; and Champlain, who explained that he would stay—"in the hope of making new discoveries toward Florida."

As he had expected, Champlain found himself given the less than easy job of picking another colony site. His first thought was of the sheltered west coast of Nova Scotia. Then he had what he believed was a better thought. He went again into the sheltered Annapolis Basin and eased up the bay to a harbor site he liked. Back of the harbor was a fertile highland and a mountain range to give protection from the freezing north winds.

When he had chosen the site, Champlain returned command of the ship to his old friend Captain Pontgrave and settled to planning a really excellent and lasting colony. He called the site Port Royal. As a first move, and using still another of his talents, he drew plans for each building and garden farm needed. His drawings were so expert and thorough that after 350 years the Canadian Government engineers had no trouble in building a replica of the Port Royal of 1605.

This time, instead of hastily built log shacks, Champlain directed the building of Norman style farm homes from logs and stones and roofed with shingles.

After the new buildings were well started, Champlain set out once more with hopes of locating the copper mines which could mean so much to France. He left Father Aubrey in temporary charge of the colony, and with Montagnais Chief Secondan and a French mine worker named Jacques Chambrun he headed the pinnace up the St. John River to find the fabled copper ores.

Again the venture was not successful, and again the home base was less than comforting. By December the snow was already a foot deep and several colonists were sick. For bad measure, the Catholic and Huguenot members were disagreeing long and loudly about sectarian matters. However, all the colonists worked together to brave the rest of the long winter. The houses were now completed. Each had at least two large fireplaces and mountains of wood had been cut and stacked for winter use. There was plenty of small game, including rabbits, ducks, Canadian geese, and plovers, a very fine game bird.

In the belief that more fresh meat would help ward

off scurvy and other illnesses, Champlain organized and led hunting parties. He also devised out-of-doors vats for freezing meat and fish.

"We could still use some moose meat," the leader noted. "In this country it's the nearest thing to beef, but we seem to to be out of the range of moose."

At that point the newly arrived head cook of the colony, a man from Brittany known as Fat Pierre Lorenz, pointed out that they also needed cooking oil. "What became of those pigs I heard about?" he demanded.

Champlain smiled sadly. "They've been eaten, alas. So have the sheep. . . . I asked for more of each to be sent over on the next supply ship."

Fat Pierre didn't seem very happy. "That won't be before next summer. It'll be no help this winter."

Chief Secondan overheard and said cheerfully that moose meat and cooking oil would be easy to get from the friendly Indians.

"We can pay them in traders' goods," Champlain said.

The interpreter shook his handsome head. "It would be better if you used the traders' goods to barter for furs and pelts to take back to France. If you will swap in this way with them, my people will be happy to *give* you moose meat and cooking oil."

Secondan, as usual, spoke truthfully. When the colonists set up what they called a swapping shed, great numbers of Indians began coming up with very fine furs, including the then most sought for beaver furs to trade for axes, hatchets, and knives. As gifts, they dragged in great quarters of moose meat, ready frozen and drawn on pole litters or drag sleds. They also carried odd-shaped containers of oil. Champlain shortly learned that these gifts were seal oil. The strangely shaped bottles or pouches were made of the dried bladders of moose.

Noting Champlain's pleasure, the interpreter said, "My people will bring you good tobacco to smoke."

Had he not been brunette and further darkened by open sun and wind, Champlain might have gone pale. He detested pipe smoking, never enjoyed tobacco in any form, and already had found the frequent smoking of peace pipes a very painful chore. All the more so because the native tobacco was very "strong."

"I like the purpose of the peace pipes," he told his friend. "But the very thought of more and more peace smokes makes me sick at my stomach."

"Maybe I could make you a smaller pipe," Secondan said. "That way as the peace offerer you could take just one small puff and pass the pipe along."

"That's fine," Champlain murmured. "But couldn't I take my puff *before* lighting the pipe?"

Chief Secondan thought for a long time. "It would not hurt to try," he said. "I will tell my people that you are a star-gazer who knows how to smoke without using live coals."

It was a very helpful suggestion which Champlain happily accepted.

But there was no way to avoid winter—or as the

"I like the purpose of peace pipes," he said.

Indians called it, the Great Hungry Whiteness. The great snows came again, piling high against the doorways and covering the little windows. Sickness also came again. February found a dozen clearly developed cases of scurvy. Only five of these recovered. Even so the death rate was only about one in seven. During the previous winter it had totalled almost one half.

Champlain worked tirelessly at his great folio of maps which included drawings of suggested ports, harbors, trading posts, forts, and, always important to the man from Brouage, locations for churches and missions. He shaped plans for exploring all the Atlantic coastline to the Spanish lands soon to be called Florida. He projected or made "educated guesses" of the sizes and locations of many great inland rivers and lakes. His guesses, like his actual surveys, were almost unbelievably accurate.

The man of so many talents drew sketches of his estimates of the Hudson River and the islands at its mouth which he had heard were peopled by Manhattan, Nassau, and other Indian tribes known to be peaceful. What are now the city and the state of New York were still unclaimed by any country other than France. Neither England nor Holland at the time had any claim on New York or any other American lands. The sharp-eyed Henry Hudson had come nowhere near the great river which would later bear his name. There was still no Nieu Amsterdam. Britain's Jamestown or James River Colony would not appear until one year later, and the landing of the Pilgrims on Cape Cod was still more than fourteen years in the future. While working through the long and not too happy winter at Port Royal, Champlain made plans for exploring the Hudson Valley and the historic islands at and near its tidewaters. If his plans had been realized, quite possibly North America would be part of France. Quite probably we would now be speaking and writing in French.

Spring came late. It was June when Commander de Monts arrived on the company's ship, *Bonne Renommee*. The Commander was pleased to see the colony had survived this winter better than the last. He congratulated Champlain on work well done and approved his plans to explore, map and claim for France all the Atlantic coast south to the Spanish lands. He also favored exploring and claiming the great river to the west (the Hudson) and its "mouth island" where the Manhattan Indians lived.

"Shall we sail our heavy ship on the exploring trip?" De Monts asked.

"I recommend taking the big pinnace boat," Champlain answered. "It would be safer in coastal waters and much less costly to operate."

"You know best," the Commander answered.

Champlain went to work rigging and supplying the eighteen-ton pinnace and selecting a crew. He chose twenty of the most able sailors, two Indians to serve as guides and interpreters, and invited De Monts to join the party. The elderly Commander accepted and happily boarded the little craft. Champlain took over as navigator and captain and, after a farewell breakfast with the colonists and Indian friends, ordered out the boat. The sea was calm. The spirits of the crew were high. Commander de Monts sat grandly in his lounge on the tiny foredeck.

But the craft had barely cleared Whitehead Island when Champlain saw his commander slump forward. He hurried to the older man who breathed hard and seemed unable to speak. The Commander's face showed an odd bluish tinge.

Because he had seen heart attacks before, Champlain hurried to make his commander as comfortable as possible on a hammock which he swung low on the two center sticks or masts. He decided to return as rapidly as possible to Port Royal where a ship's surgeon was available. He knew the resulting delay would hinder the proposed mapping and exploring trip. He also knew that the change of plans might save the Commander's life. In order to shorten the journey he resolved to swing out some twenty leagues, or seventy miles, into the never too dependable Atlantic Ocean.

He was well aware that a pinnace was not meant to be an ocean-going craft and that the short route back was dangerous, even for an expert navigator. But his commander's life was in the balance.

Presently Sieur de Monts regained consciousness and was able to speak again. "Well, Captain Samuel, I see that you are bent on trying to save my life, what can I do in return?"

Champlain was peering northeast where a bank of storm clouds was forming. "Excellency, you can pray," he answered.

Having set the foresail obliquely to the rising storm winds, Champlain led all his followers in prayer. He had barely heard the "amen" when the storm raged upon them. As wave tips sloshed the mast tops and boomed against the prow and starboard, Champlain used the last ounce of his great skill and experience to keep the pinnace afloat. After at least twelve terrible hours he managed to tack the pinnace to the side of the *Bonne Renommee* and transfer De Monts to the care of the ship's surgeon. Then he watched the supply ship muster crew and homebound passengers and set sails for France. There Commander de Monts recovered.

CHAPTER **6**

ST. LAWRENCE ADVENTURE

The summer was a happy one. But there was no news from France. Colonists who had finished their "contract year" were eager to sail for home. But no ship came. June and July passed without so much as a show of sail in the beautiful but remote harbor.

Finally, in August, a company ship arrived with supplies and new colonists. There weren't too many of either. The first batch of colonists who had lived through the terrible winter on St. Croix Island had passed out word of what an awful time they had in New France. Quite probably they had built up the hardship stories, but the gist of their reports was true, and the company had trouble recruiting another group of volunteers.

As anybody could see, the company was also hard put to find a ship. The *Jonas* was old, leaky, and rather badly kept. Its captain advised that the same held true for the trading and colonizing company. The stockholders, as usual, were grumbling that they had too few furs and too many expenses.

Champlain was disappointed by the supply ship's failure to bring a priest or, as he had requested, several priests. Captain Pontgrave explained that the company's invitation to the clergy had gone out during Holy Week when most priests were very busy hearing confessions. After that, several had shown interest in coming to New France but were not given enough time for gaining the consent of their bishops.

Champlain was also warned that several of the newest colonists were law breakers who had chosen coming to New France instead of serving a prison sentence or other dreaded punishment. But, in spite of these few, the leader found some very promising human material. He was most favorably impressed by the youngest of the newcomers, fifteen-year-old Robert de Pontgrave, the sea captain's son.

Champlain also formed an instant friendship with a Parisian apothecary or pharmacist, Louis Hebert, who was destined to head the first French family in the New World. He also particularly liked another new arrival who may well have been the first Negro to take up residence in the New World. He was Mathieu d'Acosta,

80

formerly a Portuguese fisherman who had served on fishing ships off the banks of Newfoundland and learned several of the Indian languages. This was to prove very helpful, and Mathieu d'Acosta was a kindly, hard-working man who fitted well in any group and had both intelligence and courage.

Champlain welcomed all the new volunteers. He was more than pleased to find that most of them were interested in gardening and farming. He told them earnestly: "Farming must be our gold here in New France. Whoever has corn, wine, cattle, linens, leather, iron and codfish need have naught to do with treasure hunting."

Though the summer had grown late, Champlain gave each of the newcomers a garden plot and a generous handout of seeds. "Go ahead and plant," he instructed. "Before the great frosts come, you may still grow good food. . . . And I promise you that next year we will have cattle for making good beef and good French cheese."

Early in September, the *Jonas* raised sail for France with most of the Port Royal colonists who had served out their year on board. But there was one welcome hold-over. Father Aubrey, who had planned to return to his parish in Vincennes, decided to stay on another year.

The good priest was on hand September 7, when Champlain again readied the big pinnace and, with eighteen sailors and two interpreters crowded aboard, set forth to explore the coast. Father Aubrey spoke prayers for safety, sprinkled the boat with holy water, and presented each of its crewmen with a rosary.

At St. Croix Island, Champlain paused to pay respects to the graves of the first dead of New France. He noted that the wheat, rye, and garden vegetables which had been planted nearby still grew handsomely and seeded themselves.

The explorer then headed for Cape Cod where he made a shore call to map and praise the harbor which he named Port le Bleau. On the last day of September he landed at the site of Wellfleet, Cape Cod, which he also mapped and described. Farther around the Cape, Champlain went ashore to gather wild plums, bayberries, and wild roses which he gave to his crew. One of his sailors responded by providing his commander with a "bird under glass." The sailor had fired a musket one time and felled twenty-eight of the gamey shore birds called plovers.

Then abruptly good hunting changed to bad. The boat was crowded with twenty-one people and their supplies. Understandably, Champlain's usual practice was to travel only by day, then beach the craft and spend the nights camping ashore. At twilight one day the two interpreters, both very jovial chiefs, went ashore, as they explained, to "smell out the situation." On return to the boat they recommended that the entire party spend the night aboard the pinnace.

"We can't sleep packed together like salt fish in a keg!" one sailor complained.

"We will ease the craft on the sand and take turns

sleeping," Champlain directed. "Until three bells past midnight, ten will sleep and nine stand watch. Then we will change watches."

The leader headed the first watch and in due time roused the sleepers and mustered out the relief. But while he slept five crewmen slipped away from the boat and chose more comfortable resting places on shore. It was a sad mistake. Marauding Indians came out of the night and killed three of them.

Champlain, a light sleeper, was wakened by the commotion. But before he could reach the scene with help the Indians had vanished into the darkness. At first dawn he called for volunteers to help him bury the dead. He led the service and shaped cedarwood crosses to mark the graves. The party had barely returned to the boat when the Indians returned and arrows began falling uncomfortably close.

"Get out the brass cannon!" Champlain commanded.

Strong men pulled out the blocky little deck gun which had been stashed in the aft bin. Hurriedly, Champlain poured black powder into the breechblock and struck the firing flint. He had not included shot. The little cannon spat out a great cloud of smoke and a shaking roar.

As he had expected, the marauding Indians who had never heard or seen gunfire were paralyzed with fright. At least twenty fell to earth crying or whimpering with fear. When they saw this, several of the sailors asked permission to destroy the "cowards."

"They've killed three of our comrades. Now we can

83

wipe out all the lot of them, easy as snuffing out baby birds."

Champlain spoke very firmly. "That would be murder. What you ask I refuse."

Without further comment the leader ordered the pinnace put to sea. The next stop was on the beautiful little island, Martha's Vineyard. From there Champlain pushed on to Nantucket Sound which he carefully mapped. Then he traveled down the coast of what is now Connecticut.

New York and its wonderful islands waited directly ahead. Champlain was more eager than ever to push on, befriend the Manhattan Indians, and raise the lily banner of France.

But again the season was growing late; already it was the last week in October. If he went on to the lands now covered by New York City he could not possibly get back to Port Royal that winter. Champlain faced the hard choice between two duties. He was official geographer for New France. He was also official colony leader. The geography would last. The colonists, if neglected, might and quite probably would die. Champlain made his choice. Once more he sailed north. When the pinnace pulled into the basin of Port Royal, the hills and valleys were already knee-deep in snow.

The new colonists had been hard at work. Cellars were filled with fine vegetables and attics with bags of drying grain. Woodpiles were as big as houses. A newly finished drainage canal circled the settlement, and on a nearby brook a grain mill was turning. Apothecary Hebert was busily collecting and drying wild herbs and medicinal roots.

Actually, the winter of 1606–7 turned out to be remarkably mild. Several January days were warm enough for outdoor picnics. The one regretted shortage was of red meat. Deer were scarce and the snow never grew deep enough for moose hunting. But small game, such as rabbits and squirrel, was plentiful and the fishing good. The nearby woods held plenty of nuts, berries, and Indian potatoes.

Even so, February brought another outbreak of scurvy. In all, seven men died. Champlain was deeply grieved and bewildered. He could only reason that some of his colonists had been badly undernourished before their arrival in the New World.

During the winter, Champlain founded and organized what he called the Order of Good Cheer—l'Ordre de Bon Temps. Once each week, usually on Wednesday, the Order held a luncheon or dinner meeting. The first goal was to build up the spirits of the colonists and bring the group together for good times as well as good works.

Every one was invited to the big commissary room including many of the colony's Indian friends. There was music, which ranged from Indian chants and tambourine solos to zither solos and lusty group singing which Sieur Poutrincourt led. There was always one speech.

Champlain took pains to stay in the background. Each colonist, beginning with young Robert Pontgrave, served his turn as toastmaster. Each had to earn his turn, since service as toastmaster was a reward for having contributed the tastiest dish for the previous luncheon or dinner, whether a platter of fish, or a side of venison, or a tray of wild goose or other fowl. The winner was chosen by voice vote, having entered the competition with his gift of an entree, then given a special medal or "chain of honor" which he wore proudly while serving as toastmaster.

Before his third winter in the New World was ended, Champlain developed another grand idea. This was for a series of what would now be called exchange fellowships. The gist of the plan was to bring to the New World talented youngsters from France who would volunteer to spend two or three years as what Champlain termed, "apprentices to Indian Life." (Incidentally, so far as the writer can make out, this was Champlain's first publication of the word "Indians"; previously he had called them "natives," "aboriginees," "forest people," and on occasion "savages," though it should be noted that in that era, "savage" was the usual term for any strange or foreign people.)

The colony leader recommended fifteen to eighteen as the best ages to take part in the plan. He believed that at those ages the boys would be strong enough to last through and enjoy the rugged pioneer life and still be young enough to learn languages quite easily. Language was even then a very serious barrier to friendships and understanding among peoples and nations. For the most part, the Indian languages were unwritten and extremely difficult for an adult to master.

Champlain noted that his two youngest colonists, Robert Pontgrave, the ship captain's son, and Biencourt Poutrincourt, the old soldier's son, both excelled at learning the various Indian tongues. Both the boys were then fifteen, and the leader had them tagged to be his first exchange fellows. He proposed that the colonizing company pay the costs. The company never did.

When spring came again the little colony was both peaceful and busy. Champlain no longer had to invite or urge his people to plant gardens. This time they went at the work with verve; some even dared the leader to grow vegetables as fine as those they proposed to grow. Many traded seeds with the visiting Indians.

As vegetation returned to life, Louis Hebert, the apothecary, began making a survey and a master collection of useful drugs and medicines waiting to be harvested in the nearby woods, meadows, and creek banks. Champlain was delighted. In a vast land without a single pharmacy he readily understood the importance of the project.

"We will learn to collect good medicines for our own people here," the pharmacist explained. "Then we'll send them back to France so that Frenchmen can benefit from their healing powers."

87

Champlain noted that Sieur Hebert spoke as if he meant to stay on. The apothecary meant exactly that. He had made plans to bring over his wife and two young daughters on the next supply ship. The first family of Canada was well beyond the planning stage.

Toward the end of May when the not too good ship *Jonas* showed at Port Royal, she brought a cargo mostly of bad news. The New France Company was practically bankrupt. Stockholders were pulling out of it. De Monts had lost his leadership. The Port Royal colony was being closed out. There would be no more settlers from France. All present were ordered to return. The *Jonas* was supplied to spend the summer at fishing and fur trading. But all the grand dream of a New France was herewith ended. Even the great Samuel Champlain was being dismissed.

When the ship's captain read the letter, Hebert said to the man who had done so much for the establishment of New France, "What does this mean, my friend?"

"I don't believe this report tells the whole story," he answered curtly. "I think I can guess what happened. You know of that sly court politician Sully, one of the King's councillors? He has lately been made Finance Minister and is very jealous of the money that is being spent on the French colonies. He's a shrewd man and I feel he has contrived to strike at De Monts, causing misgivings among the company stockholders about his ability."

Champlain had guessed correctly. But he also sensed

that some of the colonists would elect to stay on. Finding the group naturally upset and uncertain as to what to do, he pointed out the choices. "You can board the ship now and try a summer at fishing or fur buying, or you can stay here for the summer and choose the next step when the ship returns. Personally, I'm staying here. I have my charts and maps to finish for His Majesty and there are the gardens and crops and houses to be tended."

A little carpenter with a very large beard pressed forward: "Can't you understand plain French, Captain? There won't be any more colony. This is the end of our adventure."

Champlain faced the assembled settlers: "How many will join me in proving this isn't the end of all our work?"

Fourteen men and the two boys moved forward. In the foreranks was Father Aubrey.

In September when the *Jonas* returned with her hatches filled with furs and fish packed away in salt, the fourteen volunteers were still determined to stay on. Champlain, however, had come to a startling decision. He was going to return to France.

Father Aubrey voiced the surprise of all his companions when he said, "But we elected to remain here because we thought you would once again help us to make further progress in this wild land. What will we do without you? Who is going to lead us if you leave?"

"I am not deserting you, my good people," Champlain answered. "I will be back and when I return it will be with a group almost as fine as the one I'm leaving behind. With your example I'll now be able to choose the right kind of people to share in this great adventure. Believe me, I wouldn't have made this decision if I hadn't every faith in your strength and ability to prosper here."

Although their fears were great, the confidence their respected and beloved leader showed in them stilled any further questions. They were more determined than ever, for they now had to live up to the trust Champlain had placed in them.

Seeing that he had been able to explain his reasons to the volunteer's satisfaction, Champlain began to move his baggage aboard ship. It included bags of grain and boxes of fine vegetables grown at Port Royal. They proved the richness of the New World earth. Other baggage included a caribou, known as the Algonquin reindeer. The huge creature was very much alive and securely caged. So were the twelve Canadian geese which we are told honked and hissed all the way to France where they helped to ornament the King's lodge at Vincennes.

On October 1, the *Jonas* arrived at St. Malo. After three years and seven months, Champlain was again in his native land. When he journeyed to Paris, then Versailles, to seek audience with his King, he learned that his Majesty was away on a long carriage tour of rural France.

So Champlain went instead to Queen Marie de Medici. He asked her permission to invite Jesuits to take over the colony at Port Royal. As he had thought, the

Queen did not exactly agree but she did not say no. The already strong and famous Order of the Company of Jesus had proved greatness as colony builders and no monarch wished to deal lightly with the Order. Count de Monts, who had recovered from his heart attack but was still in frail health, offered to give over his royal appointment as Viceroy of New France to the Jesuits, provided he could hold Port Royal as his own "fief."

Here again one may suspect that Champlain had deftly planned the entire offer. As a temporary move, De Monts named Captain Poutrincourt and his young son as head of the colony during Champlain's absence. So the way was discreetly opened for both missionaries and, as Commander de Monts put it, "coureur de bois," those who found "savagery" in the New World more attractive than "civilization" in the Old World.

"Count me with the 'coureur de bois' " Champlain told his old commander. "I'm already tired of being a civilized Parisian."

"Why, Captain! I thought you loved Paris."

"I love my New France better," Champlain insisted. "I love its clean water and air and sun. I'm finding Paris crowded and loud and dirty. The red dust here clogs my lungs. And I haven't had a decent drink of water since I got here."

Commander de Monts laughed. "What's wrong then with the wonderful Parisian wines and brandies?"

"I like fresh clean water better," Champlain repeated.

De Monts laughed again. "My son, you might at least act civilized while in the great civilized city . . . I see you are still wearing the old black felt hat you must have inherited from your grandfather. Here the gentlemen, and naturally I include you among them, are wearing fine fur hats. And you know as well as I, fine furs are what will bring back my company and your colony."

As Champlain soon noted, men's hats made of fine furs, particularly brown beaver, were the "rage" of Paris. The tall headpieces were bespangled and ornamented on the right side, with the left remaining bare of gimcracks to accommodate fencing with swords. Some of the younger men of fashion were also beginning to sport capes and cloaks made of fur.

Champlain did not yield to the urge to dress like a dandy. We are told that even when he called on his King the man from New France wore the plain black garb of the middle class Frenchman. But he noted in his journals that Paris shops had windows piled with fine furs from the lands of the Algonquins and Hurons. Naturally he agreed that the fur trade was necessary for building New France, including its hope for colonies and churches.

Both English and Dutch trading companies were making great fortunes from the fur trade. Champlain wrote and presently told his King in person how the finest of all furs were forthcoming from the great north of New France. If France's part of this fabulously rich trade could be managed by a wise and good King instead

92

of a gang of greedy traders in French seaports, if it could be properly supported by more and bigger colonies, each with churches and schools made available to the natives as well as the colonists. . . .

His French Majesty Henry IV listened and agreed. He revoked his Council's action and gave back the viceroyalty of New France to the aging but still valiant De Monts. Though he had lately changed from one of the richest Frenchmen to one of the poorest, De Monts managed to reorganize the company and to lease and provision three more ships. He directed the first to return to Port Royal. The second, commanded by gay old Captain Pontgrave, made ready to go fur trading up the St. Lawrence. The third, a beautiful new ship named *Don de Dieu,* would carry a full cargo of trading goods for buying furs from the Indians. Champlain saw to it that he was assigned to the *Don de Dieu.* This time his official title read, "Lieutenant of the Forces of C. de Monts."

When the *Don de Dieu* set sail on April 13, 1608, Champlain had completed plans for founding another colony, this one to be located well up the St. Lawrence River. He had found the wife and two young daughters of Louis Hebert in Paris and made them places aboard the ship with plans for locating the apothecary and his family in the new colony.

While in Paris, Champlain had become good friends with the famous Jesuit scholar Father Pierre Biard and

He completed plans for founding another colony.

Father Cotton, another Jesuit who was the King's confessor. He had received the promise of a Jesuit priest to serve at the proposed new colony on the St. Lawrence.

On sailing day, Champlain took over his favorite shipboard assignment as navigator and once more made an excellent crossing.

When the handsome new ship reached Port Royal, Champlain was eager to see how the brave colonists he had left behind had fared. It was obvious from the appearance of the busy community that his confidence had been well placed. He gave heartfelt thanks when he saw Father Aubrey pushing through the crowd milling about the ship.

After their first greetings Champlain said, "My good and true friend, you look as if your adventures without me have suited you."

"We were able to carry on better than I had thought we could when you left. But it only proves how valuable your training was," Father Aubrey answered.

Champlain then went on to tell Father Aubrey the good news from France. "So you see, your efforts here have not gone to waste and I will be able to pursue my dream of building further glories for France in this new land," Champlain concluded.

He was impatient to be gone on his journeys, but, as always, Champlain first saw the passengers and supplies safely landed and given shelter. Then he readied an eighteen-ton pinnace for coastal and river travel. He was well aware that if New France were to live and grow it

95

would be necessary to know and colonize the St. Lawrence. The great river was already the lifestream of the now all-important fur trade. Champlain was quite certain, too, that much fertile land fronted the river. He was, therefore, resolved to found the next colony at some favorable point beside the river.

He had picked his nine companions with special care. The group included Father Natel, the priest who had been assigned to the project, four expert oarsmen, and four carpenters who also had experience as masons. As special guests he took along two Montagnais Indians to serve as interpreters.

On his third day of upriver travel, Champlain saw an area which he believed precisely right for setting up a habitation. The spot was on a highland overlooking the St. Lawrence and within a short distance of a favorable location for piers and docks. With his entire force helping, the builder of New France first set to erecting a log warehouse very near what is now the Church of Notre Dame des Victories in the old city of Quebec. The work was tremendously hard and the men had to live primitively and in the open.

By the end of the summer the colony of Quebec had twenty-three residents, all men. Working together, and none more diligently than Champlain himself, the force had completed the warehouse, three log cottages, each with a storage cellar, an outer defense wall of logs, and a canal or moat which surrounded most of the new construction. For good measure they had cleared and planted first gardens and a grain field, and Champlain had planted a vineyard of native grapes. He had also built a very ingenious sundial on a stone pillar and raised a tall flag pole. He next sewed from odds and ends of a bolt of cloth a very good likeness of the banner of Henry of Navarre, Henry IV, King of all France. On both sides of the tri-colored banner Champlain painted the symbolic lilies.

Passing Indians landed their canoes to look, admire, and visit. The newcomers had raised a village using only native materials, but the results were impressively different from the homes and villages conceived and built by the Indians of the land.

As September ended, great parties of Montagnais and other Algonquins swarmed downriver to pay their respects. As the Indian women and children gathered wild berries for winter drying, the men fished for eels which they split and smoked for use as insurance against winter hunger and also as gifts to the Frenchmen. Finding themselves showered with smoked eels, the colonists set about learning to like them. One member, Champlain's locksmith, tried too hard; he died of indigestion.

By mid-November the snows began. The Indians of the area began finding themselves running short of food. By January even the smoked eels were used up and pitiful throngs of hungry natives were tramping the valleys and banks of the frozen streams like lost and hungry sheep.

Champlain kept with his policy of everyday Christianity. The habitation had grown and harvested good crops and had been at least partially supplied by small boat cargoes from the downriver supply base. But now the great river was icebound and no more supplies could be delivered until spring.

Champlain wrote in his journal: "I ordered bread and beans to be given to them (the Indians) and did the best I could to furnish them with supplies, but it was all too little in comparison with their large numbers. . . . I consider that if anyone were to show them . . . how to till the soil . . . they would learn very well; for there are many of them who have good judgment . . . I believe they would soon be brought to be good Christians. . . ."

CHAPTER **7**

THE UNWILLING WARRIOR

Champlain made up his mind to devote his forty-first year to founding another lasting colony and building still more friendships with the Indians.

By now his list of colonists had grown to twenty-eight. They included mainly sailors, carpenters, and masons, with a clerk, five farmers or farm laborers, and six newcomers who had more or less drifted in. Of the latter group Champlain was especially pleased with two youths: Etienne Brulé, the homeless son of a fur trader, and a French-Indian lad named Nicholas Marsolet, who had come upriver as a stowaway in a fur trader's canoe. Young Brulé was then fifteen; Marsolet, sixteen.

Both boys proved themselves good workers. Both

99

showed unusual talent for getting along with the Indians and both spoke several of the north country Indian languages. This made the youngsters quite useful as interpreters. They had lived among the Indian tribes and knew and liked their ways. Both had traveled into what was called the "north country," meaning the lands along or above the Ottawa River. They knew how to gather, cook, and enjoy Indian foods, and how to sleep comfortably in wigwams, heads hubbed about the "center fire" and bodies reclining spokelike on ground pelts or robe pallets.

By Christmas Day snow was waist-deep. What was much worse, the scurvy was beginning to strike again. Within another month eighteen of the twenty-eight colonists were abed sick. For the first time in his life Champlain himself was stricken with scurvy. The colony doctor, M. Atrou, who had done double-duty as colony clerk, sickened and died of the disease.

By mid-February there were nine more deaths among the Quebec settlers. Champlain had recovered by then and was quite sure he knew the remedy—better food, including more fresh meat and green vegetables. But he now had no green vegetables and very little fresh meat to issue. Before the winter was over three more of his colonists had died. By then Champlain, "Father Jesuit," and the two bright boys, Etienne Brulé and Nicholas Marsolet were pressed into service as nurses. The leader recalled that the two youngest members had not been sick all winter.

On April 8, the great thaw began. Almost overnight

buds began appearing on trees and bushes and green grass began showing in the lingering snow. Champlain thanked God. Still weak and staggering he ventured outside to pick green buds for his followers to nibble.

When April ended only eight of his twenty-eight Quebec colonists remained. But Champlain was as determined as ever to push ahead with building New France.

This involved the fur trade and Indian friendships which were really the same resource. The background picture was unchanging. The brotherhood of the various Algonquin tribes and their strong north country allies, the Hurons, controlled the sources of practically all the fine quality furs which, of course, were found in the areas with very cold winters.

To the south, largely in what is now New York State, lived the principal tribes of the Iroquois Federation. The Iroquois were the strongest of all the Indian nations in or near New France. But their fur catches were second-rate; in Iroquois homelands the winters were simply not cold enough for the fur bearers to develop the thick, glistening coats which met quality standards. So the Iroquois had taken up two decisive occupations, farming and fighting. The latter was centered in sending war parties north to seize and capture the top quality furs which Hurons, Ottawa Algonquins and other of the great northland tribes brought down, usually by canoes, to sell—or swap—to the fur traders.

Champlain knew the general facts and had seen some of the principles. He had learned, for example, that from their homelands centered in the Georgian Bay area the

Hurons carried their splendid fur catches by canoe for distances of well over a thousand miles, including "land carries" or portages of up to fifty miles. Frequently they loaded as much as a thousand pounds of furs in a single birchbark canoe. Then by twos or threes, sometimes in fleets of as many as a hundred, the amazing voyagers would head down the great rapids of the Ottawa and other beautiful and dangerous northern streams into the great St. Lawrence and on down to Tadoussac and other trading posts on or near the Gulf of St. Lawrence or to other coastal points where white men's ships waited to barter for the furs.

On a brief upriver study trip Champlain saw what he called a "huge flotilla" of Huron canoes bounding down fierce rapids which he would otherwise have marked as impassable. Understandably, as a navigator, he admired the Hurons tremendously. He termed them the aristocrats of American Indians. But he particularly liked the Algonquin nations, including the Ottawa tribes whom he termed the New World bourgeoisie or middle class, and the Montagnais, whom he saw as the "lovable yeomen."

At Chamby Rapids Champlain came face-to-face with a most trying decision. He was confronted with what was, in fact, a notification committee. Two dozen canoes came sweeping downriver. They carried about sixty chiefs, medicine men, warriors, and other important representatives of the Hurons, the Ottawa Algonquins, and the Montagnais. An Algonquin chief stated the problem:

"Since you are our friend and since we are yours, we ask you to be our war leader against our common enemy the Iroquois. We ask you to show us how to subdue him before he destroys us."

Champlain insisted that he have time to think over his answer. The Indian leaders agreed but showed clearly that they expected him to agree to their proposal. They said they would call at his habitation within a week bringing with them a great war party, and that an even greater war party of Hurons would shortly head downriver to join them.

Champlain spent many prayerful days and sleepless nights trying to decide his course. He hated war and killing. But he knew he could not be guided wholly by personal feelings. If France's fur trade failed, New France was doomed. As an experienced soldier, Champlain believed that if he could lead a swift surprise attack, fronted by a few cannon or musket shots, an Iroquois outpost could be quickly defeated with very little bloodshed, maybe with no bloodshed at all. His aim and hope, therefore, was to end with one quick but decisive battle a far greater war which threatened to continue without end.

Early in July, 1609, Champlain received his promised Indian army. The total was only about ninety men and at least twenty of these were chiefs, medicine men, and soothsayers or advisors. The promised Huron force still had not arrived, but was expected to be waiting upriver.

Champlain led out the force. He was accompanied by

two fellow Frenchmen and colonists, Proteau and Tangifie, both veterans of the Royal French Army. The three Frenchmen went armed with huge muskets called arquebuses and weighing some forty pounds without shot or powder. The force set out by canoes as far as the headwaters of River Richelieu, thence to a place now called Rouse's Point at the head of a beautiful inland lake now known as Lake Champlain.

Before reaching the lake which was a water marker to Iroquois country, Champlain tried to give his force some basic training in white man's warfare, including drill. But the Indians were not interested in this; they had their own ideas of combat principles.

They did agree, however, to let Champlain assign patrols to keep watch along the riverbanks or lakeshores while the canoe fleet pressed ahead. The shore guards spent most of their time and energy at hunting and in this, at least, they were quite successful.

On the night of July 13, the odd little army arrived in enemy territory. The war party, mostly Algonquins, voted to take a day off for feasting and for waiting the arrival of the Huron force. The feast was magnificent. The fare included venison, bear meat, native fowl and fishes. But the promised force of Hurons did not arrive.

In a determined effort to keep the maneuver a surprise, Champlain insisted that his force hide themselves and their canoes in the woods during daytime and travel only at night. He also ordered a portage to the waters of the lake and, as usual, he carried his own equipment, which in this instance weighed well over a hundred pounds.

To the east, in what is now Vermont, he saw mountains which were still snow-capped, even in July. To the west he viewed the blue Adirondacks. He may well have been the first white man to put foot in either Vermont or New York. On the way the leader heard and recorded mention of Lake George, the Hudson River, and the lower New York coast which was then known as the Land of Norumbega.

After ten days of very cautious advance the invaders rounded the tongue of land below what was soon to become Fort Ticonderoga. At that point Champlain became quite certain that he had no advantage in terms of surprise. A canoe fleet of Mohawk Iroquois, who appeared to number some two hundred, was moving northeast, quite possibly on a fur stealing expedition.

When they saw Champlain's force, the Iroquois sped to shore and began felling trees and building a defensework of logs. Since darkness was already settling, Champlain decided to delay attack until dawn.

In a short while two Iroquois braves came paddling across stream in a birchbark canoe. One of them asked in Algonquin:

"Do you wish to fight us, and if so, when?"

An Algonquin chief answered: "Yes, and if it is all right with you, we will attack at daybreak."

The messengers bowed and turned back to their camp. Champlain, never a very good Indian linguist, turned to the Algonquin chief to ask if he had heard correctly. He had, indeed, and he was beginning to get the impression that Indian warfare was a strange kind of a game and ritual.

Across the river the Iroquois spent most of the night singing and dancing. The Algonquins called out taunts and sang their victory songs. It was all very much like a high school or college pep rally the night before the big game.

Before daybreak Champlain was quite certain his force was outnumbered at least three to one. He saw that as all the more reason to strike first. The Iroquois waited agreeably on their side of the river while the invaders loaded into their canoes. "I had only one fear at the time," Champlain recalled. "That was of drowning. I never learned how to swim."

On landing, Champlain and his two colonist volunteers shouldered their bazooka-sized muskets and began advancing. The enemy defenses were still about two hundred yards away, and the arquebuses could shoot only thirty yards. At about seventy-five yards from the log breastworks, Champlain raised his arquebus. Instantly a shower of arrows began falling on all sides of him.

Champlain then fired in the general direction of three Iroquois chiefs who were waving their fists at him. Two of them fell face downward. Champlain suspected this was from fright. He very much doubted that any musket shots carried that far.

When the arrow showers resumed, Champlain called

Champlain raised his arquebus amid a shower of arrows.

to his followers to hold their fire. The battle was turning into a bow-and-arrow skirmish. About a dozen on
each side were wounded. But nobody was killed and
the "battle" was not much rougher than a football game.

Then, quite abruptly, all the warriors ceased making
war. Champlain motioned his force to get back to their
canoes. He was mildly amused but also deeply disappointed. He knew that nothing had been decided from
a military standpoint and that similar skirmishes would
probably go on and on. What particularly worried the
swarthy little leader was that the Iroquois had not
panicked on hearing exploding gunpowder. He thought
unhappily of the time when the Indians would have
firearms of their own. He felt that the farce the Indians
called a battle had proved disastrous for the French.
Now the mighty Iroquois would consider themselves
enemies of France and allies of other enemies of France.

One fact which Champlain did not know was that
a small group of men was at that very moment headed
for the New World to begin what was to become the
most formidable blockade of the hopes and progress
of New France. Champlain clearly sensed that the island
of the Manhattans was of crucial importance to France,
but he had missed the opportunity to claim it for his
native country.

Within five weeks Henry Hudson and party would
be arriving at what is now New York City. At the time
Hudson was in the employ of the Dutch East India
Company which sought to take furs from the Manhattan Indians. The Dutch would not build a trading

post on Manhattan Island for some months, nor claim its ownership until thirteen years later. But Henry Hudson was destined, nevertheless, to open the way for both the Netherlands and Great Britain in North America.

On returning to Quebec Champlain found an order from Count de Monts commanding him to report to Captain Pontgrave as soon as possible for return to France.

Champlain left the Quebec colony, then numbering fifteen, under direction of a loyal follower named Pierre de Chauvin and set out downriver and across the sea to France. He arrived at Fontainebleau, joined his ailing commander, then reported to the King.

CHAPTER **8**

THE SURPRISING GROOM

Again the news in Paris was discouraging. There were court rumors that the King was seeking to hire Henry Hudson to colonize New France. Understandably, Champlain was not made happy by this news. The French fur trade, under company control, was still losing money. De Monts, though still ill and financially shaky, was willing to gamble for another year on changing the losing tides. Quite clearly his ace in hand was Champlain and the latter's friendship with the Indians.

But the lack of funds hindered colony development. Champlain was permitted to employ only eleven artisans, mostly carpenters and masons. He was not allowed to recruit or invite any additional settlers.

Like a good soldier, he obeyed his orders. With his small group of helpers and in company with Captain Pontgrave, Champlain set sail again and in early June arrived in Quebec. The colony was doing very well. There had been no more sieges of scurvy or other illnesses. Champlain reported that by doing without salted provisions and having fresh meat and vegetables one's chances for staying alive were fully as good in New France as in Old.

By now he had finally made up his mind to explore the northern country, up to and including Hudson's Bay. As a first step he made arrangements with a visiting chief for young Etienne Brulé to spend a year as a guest among northern Indians, specifically the Ottawa Algonquins and the Hurons. Young Brulé happily accepted the assignment. The only condition was that Champlain would presently take back with him to France a young Indian of like age for a year of study and learning in Paris.

Champlain agreed to this plan, and returned to Quebec to complete the defenses and supervise planting of grain fields and gardens. By now he found himself convinced that Quebec and New France were his real home and life.

But he was shortly obliged to visit France again. Once more the reason was unhappy. His King and friend, Henry IV, had been assassinated by a mad court follower while riding to the palace of Louvre. The new monarch of France was the boy king Louis XIII. But the actual sovereign was the dauphin's mother, Marie de Medici, who was generally regarded as cold and unpredictable and opposed to colonizing.

Queen Marie had already made clear that she was not greatly interested in New France, nor Champlain, nor even in the attractive young Huron named Savigon, whom Champlain had brought along to fullfill the terms of his agreement with the Huron chief who had taken young Brulé into his home. Savigon, too, was about fifteen and eager to learn of the ways of other peoples. What he was about to learn of Paris was not too encouraging.

France was deeply shaken by the tragic death of Henry IV. The New France Company was again deep in trouble. Dutch and British furs were pouring in on the better French markets. The worried stockholders of the French company would agree only to underwrite one more year of the various work it was pledged to do.

With Savigon as his traveling companion, Champlain sailed to his native town to visit his now widowed mother. His father had died at sea years before. After several pleasant days in the old stone cottage fronting the sea, Champlain and his young Indian friend returned to Paris.

There he told his dwindling list of friends an item of personal news which surprised them very much. Champlain, at forty-three, was getting married. And his chosen bride was only twelve!

We do not know just how or when he had met the pretty little Parisienne. We do know her name was Helene Boullé. She was the daughter of Nicholas Boullé, a well-to-do Paris shopkeeper of a good middle-class family. The wedding took place on December 30, 1610, in the revered Church of St. Germain l'Auxerrois, facing the Louvre Palace. It had been the parent church of several French kings, including the great Henry IV.

The wedding contract, dated December 27, 1610, was witnessed by Champlain's friend and superior, De Monts. Its terms are quite revealing. Nicholas Boullé, the bride's father, granted a dowry which would now be about $75,000. Champlain matched this with his own total resources, barely one-fourth that amount. He declined, however, to accept any part of the dowry. Later all the money was given to a nunnery.

The wedding contract listed the groom as a "Noble homme" and gave his name as Samuel de Champlain, his father's as Antoine de Champlain, "Captain in the Navy." There seems to be no record of Antoine's ever having been a captain in the Royal Navy of France. He was by many accounts just a respected captain of fishing boats.

The wedding was a happy and handsome one. Guests included the Indian youth and several members of the court. One biographer suggests that the boy king of France looked on from the Louvre courtyard while making snowballs.

After the ceremony, the couple and Champlain's

Indian guest moved to the home of the bride. Barely two months later, Champlain sailed from the port of Honfleur for Quebec. He left his bride with her parents; she attended a convent school nearby. But Savigon, the young Huron, insisted on returning to New France with his great friend.

The return voyage led through violent storms and great floes of ice. The ship encountered huge bergs which stood higher above the ocean than any tower in Paris—250 feet or more. Off Grand Banks, in fog so heavy one could not see the length of the ship, Champlain met one of his most harrowing adventures:

"As each one committed himself to God, thinking we should never escape the danger of that iceberg which was already under our bowsprit, we shouted to the helmsman to bear off. The great mass of ice was driving before the wind so fast that it passed close to our vessel without striking it, but the ship stopped as if to let it go by. Although we were out of danger, yet each one's blood cooled down slowly from the fright we had; and we praised God for having delivered us. . . ."

Again Champlain traveled up the St. Lawrence by pinnace. All was well at Quebec. Thanks to a good supply of fresh meat and vegetables the entire company was free of scurvy. Champlain made ready to survey the northern country and to deliver Savigon safely to his family.

Upriver from Quebec, Champlain, with the Huron youth as one of his able helpers, set out to select a site for a second colony on the St. Lawrence. This one grew into Montreal, the metropolis of Canada. Once again Champlain selected a plot of rich land, with open meadows for pasturing cattle (which had not yet arrived) and ample areas for fields, gardens, and orchards. He called the location Place Royal. It lies directly back of what are now the famous piers of Montreal, and partly on the site of the Old Customs House in that city.

After making test plantings of rye, wheat, and beans, Champlain selected a river island on which to build a defense outpost. It is now a public park just below the famed Jacques Cartier Bridge.

While Champlain and his helpers were busily marking out the new colony site, his young Huron friend Savigon and another young Huron and a Montagnais chief who were also visiting the outpost asked permission to journey ahead into the northern lands called Huronia.

Champlain gave permission. He had confidence in the young Indians as canoe travelers, as in other skills, and he knew the Huron youngsters were very eager to get home. Though he had planned a journey to Huronia himself, Champlain knew he would be held at the colony site for several months since he was hurrying to complete a fur trading post nearby.

Within a week young Savigon returned afoot and in great distress. His canoe had capsized in the Lachine Rapids. Savigon was able to swim out. Both of his companions were drowned.

Champlain promptly loaded his young friend into a small boat and hurried upriver to the scene of disaster. He held hopes that one or both of Savigon's friends might have survived. If that were not the case, he at least hoped to give the young Indians Christian burial.

But neither of the hopes was realized. Champlain understood why while viewing the huge and thunderous rapids which he named the St. Louis Rapids. As a professional navigator he simply could not see how any canoe could ride down the rapids, much less press up them.

"You are a good canoe man," he assured Savigon. "But in such a deathtrap as this I'd say it's a miracle that you saved your own life."

"My people have been canoeing those rapids for a thousand years," the young Huron answered. "They have been blessed with a million miracles."

Champlain smiled. "Spoken like a true Christian, my friend. I am pleased at the understanding you have of the ways of my people."

Savigon smiled back. "I will show you how much I have learned by helping you here until you are ready to visit my Huronia."

He was as good as his word. The middle-aged leader and the youth worked together building a fine trading post. A great canoe fleet of Hurons called to celebrate the event and gave Champlain many furs as presents. He hurriedly dispatched the big pinnace downriver to bring back a load of hatchets, cloth, bolts, knives, and other trader goods. The upcountry Indians were eager to trade beaver pelts for the merchandise, but they continued to bring generous gifts of fine furs and wampum, or Indian shell money.

The leader's happiness was tinged with sorrow when he was obliged to part with Savigon, but the youth wanted to go home, and now there were many Huron canoes which were homebound. "He is an Indian and is entitled to live the life of an Indian," Champlain explained to another follower. "I am only sorry I could not have him with me a while longer."

As soon as his work permitted, Champlain made his first extensive trip into the north country. He chose to go by canoe and alone. Upriver, he portaged around the great St. Louis or Lachine Rapids. But on the return trip, even though he still had not learned how to swim, he boldly headed his canoe into the mighty rapids. He came out of them wet, triumphant, and very much alive. Thus Samuel Champlain could tell of being perhaps the first white man to "shoot" the Lachines by canoe.

Upon his return Champlain continued to work hard building up the fur trade. Downriver from what is now Montreal he set up another trading post. It was instantly successful. Next Champlain planned and brought into being the first trading fair which was thereafter held annually for many years to come. All participants were welcome.

He set forth on horseback to Paris.

Surely now the French fur trade would prosper!

Champlain sensed that it was time now to return to France and ask for more men and supplies and gain further authority to explore the American North; he also wanted to request a company of soldiers to safe-guard the filling storages of furs. On the way down-river he stopped at Quebec to make sure his first St. Lawrence colony was readied for another winter.

Late in August, Champlain set sail for La Rochelle, the "picture port" of France. On arriving he indulged in a first time luxury; he bought himself a riding horse. On horseback he happily set out for his old hometown, Brouage. After being feted, the homecomer again spent some days with his mother and visited the Recollect monks of the Brouage monastery. Champlain was hope-ful that they might agree to set up a mission in Quebec.

He promised to personally take the case to the royal court and so set forth on horseback on the great Western Highway to Paris. There he would meet his bride and at Fontainebleau, he hoped, the Queen.

As Champlain rode along the wide road, he was lost in thoughts of the many plans he had for the future of New France. He was unaware that his horse's pace had slowed somewhat and was taken completely by surprise when the animal, with a great lurch, stumbled and fell. He did not have time to leap clear before both horse and rider crashed to the earth, the weight of the horse crushing Champlain's right leg. He was stunned and at first felt fortunate that he had not been pinned under the dying animal. However, as the pain from his leg began to increase, Champlain realized that he was in grave trouble.

In his agony, Champlain did not know that he was speaking aloud to the lonely, dusty road:

"Mon Dieu, what am I to do now? I have traveled the wild lands of the cold country for years, but never have I been as alone as I am now. I can only hope that a party will come along soon, or I shall surely die."

But as the time crawled on and the day began to turn into evening, Champlain knew he would have to take matters into his own hands. He could not last through the night without attention to his leg.

With the strength gained from many winters of primitive living and a will that would never admit defeat, Champlain started to drag himself along the road. As had happened so often before, luck was on his side, for only a few miles further on he found an inn. Although the hostelry was wretched and uninviting, to the agonized man who had just finished a journey of incredible physical endurance, it looked like a palace.

As he was inching his way through the filthy inn-yard, the door burst open and a burly fellow yelled, "We don't want any of you scurvy beggars here!"

Champlain could only feebly beckon the fellow closer and, in a weak voice, whisper, "I am no beggar. I am Samuel de Champlain. I was on my way to see the Queen at Fontainebleau when I had an accident. I cannot use my right leg."

The ugly innkeeper, at least Champlain guessed he

was the innkeeper, threw back his head and roared with laughter.

"You, to see the Queen? Get up, you dog! If you're not a beggar, then you're a highwayman!"

By this time Champlain had lost consciousness and the innkeeper drew nearer to the prone figure. On closer inspection even this hard-hearted ruffian could see that the figure lying on the ground was indeed in a bad way. Against his better judgment, he picked the wounded man up in his arms and carried him into the house.

There were only a few guests at this hour of night and they crowded around the innkeeper and his burden.

"Where did you get that, Gustave?" said one of them.

"I saw him come into the yard from the window, leaning on a stick, half walking, half crawling toward my place. I went out to order him away, when he fell flat and seems to have fainted."

Gustave had laid Champlain on one of the long tables and was looking at him through narrowed eyes.

"He's hurt all right. Look at that leg. It's a terrible sight."

"Maybe you had better get a priest," one of the lodgers said.

"A priest. Where would I get a priest at this hour? No, I will take care of him myself. He said he was on his way to see the Queen. I laughed then, but now I think he might have been telling the truth. His clothes are simple, but of good cut. He has the look of a gentleman about him. Gustave Dubois has never let an opportunity go by to make a little money and perhaps gain some favor from a man who knows the Queen."

Champlain had no choice except to lodge in the wretched hostelry. When he regained consciousness he found himself in an attic room on a grimy pallet with his leg roughly bound up. He could not move for the effort to get to the inn had further damaged the leg. He was also running a high fever.

For almost a month he lay on his dirty pallet fighting the battle between life and death. The innkeeper was of little help for he was an ignorant man with no knowledge of the gentle art of aiding the sick. It was, in fact, a miracle that Champlain's fever finally broke and he was able to take what doubtful nourishment Gustave provided. Because of the condition of his leg and the poor nursing he received, it took another two months before he was ready to move about. By that time he felt that he must be on his way to Paris, and in spite of his still-healing leg he set out on his journey. The effort was doubled for he had spent all his money for the unwished-for stay at the country inn and had none left for paying stagecoach fare or renting a horse. It took him ten days to *walk* to Paris.

When he arrived at the home of Merchant Boullé, the traveler found his bride playing happily in the yard with her nine-year-old brother, Eustache. Helene's doll carriage waited nearby. When the very young bride recognized her husband, she cried out with joy, called his name, then hurriedly drew the doll carriage behind a hedge. That done, Helene came bounding into her husband's arms.

Champlain felt all his worries lifted from his shoulders. "You have grown to be a very beautiful young lady," Champlain told his bride. "Seeing you makes me young again. I am so very happy you are my wife."

"My school girlfriends all think I'm very lucky to be your wife," Helene answered. "They are all green with jealousy because I have such a famous husband. Every girl I know wishes she were the wife of Samuel Champlain."

Next day Count de Monts was less happy than the thirteen-year-old bride, Helene. The New France Company was still in serious trouble. The stockholders, for the most part wealthy merchants from various port cities, had again refused to advance another *sou*. De Monts had managed to borrow money to buy out most of the stockholders. He was practically the owner of the company.

With Champlain's help the old man planned another kind of colonizing company. He would make it an association and admit members willing to pay fees for the right to deal in furs and pelts from the New World. The membership fees would be used to equip the three settlements, pay passages of new settlers, and support missions and churches which Champlain was determined to see established.

"I'm too old to take on all this work myself," De Monts pointed out. "And you will be too busy to do all of it. So I will try to get the King's Council to approve this plan and to appoint another viceroy. You will be Assistant Viceroy in Charge of New France."

"That is a great honor, sir," Champlain said.

"Stuff and nonsense," his old commander replied. "It's no more than you've been doing all along. But you would get along better if you had a better title."

The King's Council approved, as did even the new head of Finance, Jeannis. The Council appointed Prince de Condé as the new Viceroy; Champlain, the Assistant Viceroy.

"Your official pay for the coming year will be a horse worth a thousand crowns," the Finance superintendent announced.

Recalling his adventure with a horse on the way to Paris, Champlain shook his head politely.

"Excellency, I will serve this coming year for the love of France. Our outbound ship is ready loaded with colonists and priests and cattle. Besides, I am heading back for moose country."

The Boullés, Champlain, and his bride, Helene, decided together that Helene would remain with her parents another year while finishing the convent school she was then attending, and perhaps join her husband in New France the following year.

Viceroy Prince de Condé was very busy with social duties and instructed his assistant to write his own directives. Well pleased by this, Champlain wrote out his own orders:

You will live in the Quebec Habitation and build there a garrison and other forts as needed.

You will justify your right as here granted to commission officers, establish a system of justice, make alliances and trade treaties with the native princes.

You are directed to make explorations and discoveries, particularly in the St. Lawrence Basin.

You are to subject all peoples of New France to the authority of His Majesty and to instruct them in the knowledge of God and the Catholic Faith.

This surprising explorer was now the real ruler of New France.

CHAPTER **9**

SUNLIGHT AND SHADOWS

The winter in Paris went quite happily. Though Champlain had a great deal of work to do in connection with organizing the new "association," he also found time to spend with his bride. When a sea chest which he had filled with presents for her finally arrived, Helene was able to dress herself in the wedding garb of an Algonquin princess or great chief's wife. The beaded sandals, doeskin tunic, wampum girdle, porcupine quill necklaces, and beaver fur cape were all quite beautiful and to Parisians most astonishing.

Helene was very proud of her wonderful new outfit, but much prouder of her husband who at long last was being recognized in Paris as a man of importance—not just another explorer and author.

When the great three-day festival celebrating the betrothal of France's boy king to Spain's first princess was held at Place Royal, the Champlains were among the honored guests. And they were dressed as an Algonquin sagamore and princess. It was the social high point of both their lifetimes.

But as winter grew later and waterfowl began to fly north from the swampy Riviera and chestnut trees began to bud in Paris, Champlain found himself feeling the lure of his beloved New France.

By the end of April, Champlain was once more at Tadoussac, the supply base on the mouth of the St. Lawrence. Indians swarmed aboard to welcome their returning friend. "You are my people now," he told his welcomers. "Your dreams are mine."

At the Quebec Habitation the colonists' gardens were already showing as green rows and millions of flowers were blooming. Champlain was delighted to find that most of the colonists seemed satisfied with their new lives. He decided to take the opportunity to push into the northern lands again and get better acquainted with the Hurons and other tribes of the Algonquins. This was in the line of duty, but it was also in keeping with his personal wishes. Huronia and other northern lands were drawing him like a great magnet. At Quebec he bought and readied two strong canoes and supplied them with four strong men, all French colonists, an Indian guide, and two interpreters.

The journey was difficult but most interesting. The first hair-raising adventure took place in the great rapids of Chute a Blondeau when both canoes were sucked into a huge whirlpool. All members came out alive, however, and presently recovered the canoes and most of their belongings including a large collection of gifts for northern country chiefs.

"God's mercy preserved us all," Champlain summarized.

By early June the party reached the site of the present capital of Canada, Ottawa, then paddled on into the almost heavenly valley of Lac Deschenes.

There were many portages. Though no longer a young man, Champlain continued to carry his share of the baggage. On a fifty-mile hike the leader carried three paddles, three heavy arquebuses, a mapping instrument called an astrolabe, plus all his personal belongings. The total weight was about two hundred pounds; Champlain weighed about a hundred and fifty.

The expedition kept going ahead. From time to time the voyagers stopped to set up crosses bearing the fleur-de-lis of France. As usual Champlain painted the lilies. Again and again friendly Indians swarmed down to greet the unexpected travelers and make feasts for them.

Champlain noted that feasts of welcome had become daily or twice-a-day events. Ottawa Algonquins and Hurons alike heaped the visitors with gifts. When the canoes began to show wear, the travelers found themselves given new canoes. "I spend most of my time

The total weight was about two hundred pounds.

thanking my friends and my Greatest Friend, the Almighty," Champlain wrote. He was especially thankful because "the natives have accepted two more honest and truthful youths to be educated in their language and hardihoods. . . ."

It was a wonderful summer and Champlain was quite willing to list 1613 as the happiest year of his life. But his journals indicated that he had other plans quite clearly in mind. While on the northern journey, he was giving careful attention to possible sites for missions and churches.

On returning to Quebec Habitation, Champlain made a quick change of plans and boarded the supply ship outbound for France. Apparently he had heard that the new association, now renamed the Compagnie des Merchands, was once more in trouble.

In a deft move to rouse greater public interest in the plight and promise of New France, Champlain turned in his geographer's report to the new King. Then, with great competence, he prepared and published still another book, *Voyages du Sieur Champlain*. The work was illustrated with the author's superb pen drawings and maps. Many scholars still regard it as the best published work on American Indians. The author went beyond this to strongly urge better protection of New France from rival colonizing powers, especially England and Holland, and better management of the fast-growing fur trade. But the special point was to stress the need for helping the Indians to a better understanding of Christianity. "They are living without faith," he repeated. "I would be doing very wrong if I did not work to find some means to bring them to the knowledge of God. . . ."

While his new book was finding readers, Champlain moved to recruit missionaries for service in the New World. Following plans carefully laid, he again traveled to his native town to urge the Recollect Friars of Brouage to move to New France.

However, the Recollects were a brotherhood of strictly maintained poverty. They had neither money nor means for earning it. Even so, the abbot and brother provincial tramped barefoot to Paris (no member wore shoes) to seek the required permissions of their bishop and the cardinal.

Permission was granted. With effort Champlain managed to raise fifteen hundred livres, in present-day values about two thousand dollars, to finance the first mission. The money was barely enough to support four of the Brothers. But the first four were the very finest of the fine old Order: Fathers Joseph le Caron, instructor in the faith for the young king and presently to be one of the truly great New World missionaries, Denis Jamet and Jean d'Olbeau, and Brother Pacifique du Plessis.

Though he had hoped for a much larger group, Champlain was most thankful for the first four. In this period of preparation the number four seemed to be the leader's special symbol. He asked for a company of soldiers and received four. He also asked for a herd of cattle and received four cows.

Other requests were answered more generously. The

King's Council rechartered the company for eleven years, with Prince Condé as its senior officer and Viceroy for New France. Champlain was made "Lieutenant Viceroy." Each holder of a license for fur trading was ordered to support six families of colonists for their first year in the New World.

Champlain was deeply grateful for each of the gains. He was especially delighted with the four Recollects. All were good travelers and inspiring company. They were no sooner landed at Quebec when Father d'Olbeau and Brother Pacifique set about building a chapel for the colonists there. Father Jamet joined Champlain for the next lap of upriver travel to plan and consecrate the first church in Montreal. Father Joseph le Caron promptly set out as a missionary to the far north. With almost unbelievable courage, the most famous of the Recollects joined a party of homebound Hurons on their long and dangerous upriver journey.

When Champlain offered to go along, Father Joseph shook his head: "Do your dutiful work here, my son. I will go directly to mine. These children of God also have souls. No time can be wasted in bringing them to the knowledge of Christ and the hope for Paradise. . . ."

Champlain found plenty to do. On the less encouraging side he learned that the great Iroquois Federation grew bolder and more persistent in its business of furlifting. By now Dutch traders in Nieu Amsterdam, soon to be renamed New York by its British captors, were offering more barter goods for furs than the French traders felt able to. With this incentive the

Iroquois were extending their raids on the various trapper villages of the Algonquins and seizing greater numbers of southbound canoes loaded with furs being drawn to market by Hurons.

As Champlain worked to build and man new trading posts for the advantage of France he was surprised and inspired by the effectiveness of the new missionaries. Late in July on the shores of the Great Rapids, Fathers le Caron and Jamet joined in celebrating what was almost certainly the first formal Mass to be sung in the St. Lawrence Valley. On July 26, a first Mass was celebrated at the Quebec Habitation.

Champlain was delighted and deeply touched. He reported how great throngs of Indians came to look on, as he said, "in admiration of the sight of the ceremonies and of the ornaments which seemed to them so beautiful, the like of which they had never beheld. . . ."

Champlain continued to hear and feel the call of the great northern country. There were still dozens of tribes to be met and befriended. And there was a challenge to know, see, and understand.

Once more the leader prepared, as he said, to make contact with the upper wilds. At Quebec he called for volunteers. Ten good men volunteered. Once more young Etienne Brulé and Thomas Godefrey went along to serve as interpreters. As before, the leader decided to travel by canoes with which it was easier to make the many portages and with a cargo principally of gifts and trade goods and only a very few muskets.

The first thousand miles north was another story of hard work, views of breath-taking beauty, and warm greetings by the Indians. Between feasts the travelers fed themselves. Like the far-traveling Indians they drew fishing lines in wake of the canoes. They took in the catches, dressed the fish, and, at night camps, pounded the catch with corn meal to make a kind of fish mush called *sagamite*. This was a popular fare of the Indians. The voyagers also gathered the sweet big blueberries, raspberries, plums, and many other wild fruits which grew along the riverbanks. At night they slept on the bare earth, using stones for pillows.

Progress of travel was quite rapid. In spite of the many time-consuming portages the party traveled nine hundred miles upstream in the first three weeks. While crossing the great Georgian Bay the two canoes covered two hundred miles in three days. Champlain regarded this as a canoeing record. On their seventeenth day out of Quebec the voyagers reached Lake Nipissing, which was the home of the sorcerers or "magic people" of the Northern Algonquins.

From that amazing place Champlain resolved to push on to the great lake known as the Fresh-Water Sea of the Hurons. But he found that another Frenchman had viewed Lake Huron almost a week earlier when the valiant Father le Caron had visited and blessed the fresh-water sea.

By August the great explorer and his party were at last in the country called Huronia. Once more throngs of Indians, Champlain vowed they were the most beautiful humans he had ever seen, lined the riverbanks shouting *Ho, Ho, Ho* and gesturing welcome. In what is now Simco County, Ontario, the voyagers visited a Huron city of at least thirty thousand people. They saw dozens of other towns, each one surrounded by far-spreading fields of corn, and oversize gardens of peas, beans, and squashes. It was a fairytale land. Yet it was as real as the faith of Father Joseph le Caron whom Champlain kept on overtaking.

Anyone could see that Father le Caron was moving on spiritual as well as physical power. At a Huron city called Carhagouha, the Indians had built a log and bark-roofed cabin especially for the use of the Recollect Father. In this humble shelter the valiant missionary set up a wooden cross and sang the first Mass ever heard in what is now Canada's great province of Ontario.

On arriving at the scene Champlain said in effect: "You are a better man than I am, Father Joe."

While learning the ways and moods of the great Hurons, Champlain kept on developing some of his own beliefs. For one item, he saw still more convincing cause for extending his plan for exchange fellowships for talented young men. He repeated that gifted youths are not only the most effective peace makers but the best ambassadors in the real meaning of that word, which is one who lives and represents the land of his birth in a foreign nation and knows and appreciates both his native land and the one in which he serves.

Champlain was clearly aware that Indian life was

changing. These were intelligent and spirited people moving directly from their localized stone age into an age of iron tools and weapons and foreign trade. Only intelligent youth could keep pace with the great change which was surely coming.

The thoughtful explorer noted other important facts of Indian life. He noted rather sadly that the farther north he got, the more he heard of the "great strife to the south." By that, of course, Champlain meant the worsening behavior of the Iroquois.

He kept hearing of more recent and bolder Iroquois invasions of Algonquin lands and more and more daring robberies of Huron fur canoes. "The Great Red Cuts," one Huron chief told his honored guest, using the term frequently applied to the Iroquois, "are as many as the forest leaves. . . . They have not just war parties, but great armies which break into a hundred parts, each one devil-led to pillage our fine fur catches and destroy our allies the Algonquins, and in time ourselves."

Listening chiefs agreed with emphatic nods. "What would *you* do about that, Great Frenchman?" one demanded.

Champlain answered: "Only to build and keep strong the friendship between the mighty Hurons and your great and good allies, the Algonquins, and all the other good and peaceful tribes all the way to the Western Ocean or Great Salty. . . . And my people from the Land Beyond the Great Salty are always eager to be among all the nation of friends. . . ."

The answering *Ho, Ho, Hos* were loud enough to be heard, but did not ring with conviction. The reason for the not too enthusiastic agreement was as well known to the chiefs as to Champlain. There were more than a few petty quarrels between clans and villages in the far north. Even among the Hurons, whose central government was quite democratic and greatly admired by Champlain, there were some feuds, spats, and unnecessary quarrels.

Champlain plead with the rapidly growing list of his chief or sagamore friends to join in discouraging these petty quarrels. As a venture in giving active help to this cause, he organized in Huronia a kind of committee he called the "Twelve Peace Ambassadors." Eleven of the group were chiefs, including both Huron and Ottawa Algonquins. The twelfth member was the young Etienne Brulé, whom, as we have noted, Champlain had brought along as an interpreter. The worthy job of the "Peace Ambassadors" was to visit the villages and outposts where quarrels were in progress and settle the spats—usually by arbitration or persuasion.

Yet as he headed back to home base after what was beyond any question the most successful of all his good will tours, Champlain was painfully aware that the farspread strife between the mighty Iroquois and the Algonquin-Huron allies was growing rapidly worse. Iroquois raiding parties were ranging over a quarter of a million square miles and reducing the northern fur trade to a mere trickle of what it deserved to be. The

Indian Allies pointed out with hard logic that they were already being impoverished. Very soon the Iroquois would have them enslaved.

More and more of the northern country chiefs were saying: "We must face the mighty enemy. And since you are our great friend, you must also be our war leader."

As he returned to the St. Lawrence, Champlain was met by a respected friend and, admittedly, a most able leader of the Algonquins. This was the sagamore Iroquet. The great chief and warrior leader said that he already had an army of at least seven hundred brave warriors, including two hundred visiting Hurons, all ready to go forth and do battle against the Iroquois.

"You are the man to lead us," Iroquet insisted.

Once more Champlain tried to think out the best course. As before, he knew that New France simply could not survive without its close friendship with the Algonquins and Hurons. Yet certainly the great French allies could not wage full scale war against the Iroquois and reasonably hope to win. They outnumbered the allies at least two to one. The Iroquois now had, via the Hudson River, an outlet to an ocean which did not freeze over in winter. And the Iroquois also had the Dutch and, at least in prospect, the British as allies.

Champlain retreated into the forest and thought and prayed. Once more he could see only one chance of winning and he knew it was a dim chance. But if the Algonquin-Hurons, with the help of French firearms could move quickly and powerfully to deal one sharp defeat to the mighty enemy, perhaps this time the Iroquois would realize they would be better off living within their own quite adequate boundaries. After all, they were already very successful as a farming nation. In time their fur catches, even if not of first quality, would be saleable.

Even so, Champlain found himself pained by his own "logic." He had tried the move once before and had not succeeded. He knew that the chance for winning was not even a breakeven or "fifty-fifty." But he also knew he had no immediate means for keeping peace with the Iroquois. He still believed that in time, perhaps a lifetime, peace could be, as he said, "preached and prayed" to reality. But the tides of destiny were running fast. Long before the New World could be made a Christian world, all France's necessary allies could be destroyed.

In great loneliness Champlain made his decision. He would try again to lead a striking force. Once more the leader of New France planned well and met nightmarish difficulties.

To begin with, the promised force turned out to be about five hundred warriors, not seven hundred and again the Hurons did not arrive in time.

Wisely, Champlain moved out his force by canoe fleet. With great skill he chose a water route for most of the trip to Lake Ontario. The great canoe fleet skimmed over the "fresh-water ocean." While landing his force at a point near what is now Stony Point the Frenchman viewed the gay autumn colors with a most unusual sadness. He was unhappy about his mission and he now wished he could have begun several weeks sooner.

This time he knew he was obliged to move stealthily and in hiding.

"From here we will portage," he said. "We will keep in the densest forests we can find. I expect every man to carry his own weight, as I will do. Don't scrape canoes against the trees or ledges. Don't throw away any paddles. . . . There'll be no time for hunting."

As he directed his force into the great forests, Champlain revised his orders to the extent of having the canoes hidden in dense brush. In case his force should be ambushed, he wished to keep the canoes as ready as possible.

"Check your bows and shoulder them," he commanded.

He then instructed his followers to spread apart and take all available protection. But from the first Champlain was disappointed with the progress of his "army." In open violation of orders the warriors took time to hunt and prepare a feast.

Grimly Champlain led on toward the valley of the Oneida River. As the attack group moved deeper into what all knew was enemy territory the leader tried to speed up the advance. He was not very successful. Near the present site of Brewerston, New York, a group of the Algonquin warriors attacked an outlying Iroquois village and captured ten of its residents, including two women and four children. Since he had given no permission for this, and knew the act was both cruel and foolish, Champlain hurried to the place where he found Sagamore Iroquet who was not only permitting but taking part in torturing the prisoners.

Confronted with the awful sight, Champlain was speechless for a moment. Then, his anger beyond control, he sprang at the prisoners with drawn knife in hand. The Indians were pleased for they thought their brave champion was going to join them in the gruesome game. Much to their surprise, however, Champlain cut the writhing captives from the stakes and gently laid them on the ground. He then turned on his stunned compatriots and said through clenched teeth, "What savagery is this? Have I not told you before that I will not have you torturing prisoners? If you ever try this again, you will have to fight me first!"

Iroquet and his men seemed greatly surprised at Champlain's words. They had never seen the swarthy little Frenchman angry before. The Algonquins ceased laughing as their unhappy captives ceased screaming.

"Prisoners are meant to be tortured," Iroquet explained. "If these prisoners were our own people, and the Iroquois were the captors, they would be torturing our people much more severely than we are punishing theirs. After all, we were only cutting off a few fingers."

"Get out of here!" Champlain shouted. "Get back to your places! You're supposed to be warriors. I promise you a chance to show whether you are or aren't."

The unhappy war leader commanded his force to head for what he knew was the sizable Iroquois town directly ahead. It was peopled by the Onondaga Iroquois. By then Champlain had decided that he would not wait longer for the Huron "army" which still had not appeared. Instead he readied his great musket and hurried to the head of the attack column. The Onondaga village was completely surrounded by a log barricade. From a nearby hillside Champlain could see many warriors; he estimated at least two to his one.

From all appearances the Onondagas were expecting the attack and were prepared for it. No messengers came out to discuss terms or to agree on battle procedures. Champlain reflected that in a very short time Indian warfare had ceased being a game. He hoped that the Iroquois would still be frightened by the great noise of white man's firearms. He knew that in this he was taking a considerable chance. He soon learned that play was futile.

Motioning his followers to take position for attack he hurried forward, raised his heavy arquebus, and fired the oversize "thunderstick." Nobody fell down in fright. Instead the defenders let fly a cloud of arrows.

Champlain called for a temporary retreat. He led his main force back into the forest, leaving only a thin line of bowmen to hold the Onondagas inside their own log walls.

"We will have to fire the wall and take over the village," he told his assembled chiefs. "We'll have to shield our way getting there."

Without explaining further he directed the warriors to take hatchets, which most of them carried at their belts, and help him fell trees. Then they began building what Champlain called a shield block. It was a kind of scaling platform consisting of a split log floor, a shield of split logs placed upright, and a hastily built ladder with which to climb over the defense wall. Champlain had built and used shield blocks while a Navarre soldier in the war in Brittany. He now saw the chance to use the ancient device as a winning weapon.

"Even if we can't get enough men over the wall," Champlain explained, "we should be able to get close enough to set fire to the barricade. If we can do that, they'll probably surrender."

As he began tying the timbers with leather thongs which he had providently included in his own knapsack, the leader got the impression that most of his own force and all the Onondagas were standing by to watch him work.

When the scaling platform was completed, Champlain mustered a force of strong braves to carry the cumbersome thing to the circle of barricading logs. He appointed a bow and arrow force to defend the carriers as best they could and ordered the rest of his force to circle out and surround the village.

The strategy did not work very well. The Onondaga warriors began showering arrows from platforms placed directly behind their defense walls. Champlain produced several pine torches and fired them with steel and flint. When Algonquin warriors succeeded in getting the scaling platform within a few feet of the log wall about the village, enemy warriors came pounding down upon them. Boldly, Champlain grasped two of the burning torches and tried again and again to set fire to the defense wall.

He was not successful. The battle grew fiercer. The attackers were being thrown back. Champlain continued to fire his oversize musket. But the defenders would not be frightened by it. He saw his force retreating and two Algonquin chiefs and some fifteen warriors go down with arrow wounds.

Vainly but bravely, Champlain tried to rally his force. But the Onondaga Iroquois now had all the defender's advantages and they were using the advantages. Their braves increased the rain of arrows. Champlain marveled that his force had been able to endure as well as it had. Perhaps the greater marvel was that Champlain had by now remained unhurt for almost three hours. But this good fortune could not long continue.

"We must get our wounded to safety," he called out to a Montagnais Algonquin chief who had been serving as his interpreter. "Go and fetch the shoulder frames!"

"Shoulder frames" were a sort of portable chairs which the Algonquins used for carrying the wounded or sick. The carriers, which were shaped like the frames of small, crudely built chairs, were small enough to be strapped about a warrior's shoulders. The wounded or sick man was placed in a crouching position facing to the rear of his carrier. Usually he was bound tightly into position.

The shoulder frames were more or less standard battle equipment. In bow-and-arrow warfare many more were wounded than killed. The effectiveness of any war party was partly measured in its ability to rescue its wounded who would otherwise be slain or enslaved by the enemy. By using the shoulder frames a wounded man could be carried at a run or fast walk and this was a great advantage over stretchers or similar rescue devices. Champlain was aware that his force would probably be pursued, and he was determined to save as many as possible of his wounded followers.

"Begin picking up the wounded," he directed. "We'll try to pin back the enemy with arrow fire while you get your men to backpacking."

Champlain hurried forward to realign his bowmen. At that point good fortune failed him. He felt an enemy arrow cut deep into his right thigh. As he stumbled another arrow pierced the cartilages of his left knee. Fainting with pain, the leader succeeded in pulling the arrow from his thigh but was unable to remove the other one.

By then he was aware of being lifted to a chair frame strapped to the shoulders of a towering warrior. Others were tying him in the carrier with leather thongs. For the time he was speechless with pain. Later he wrote: "It was impossible to move more than a little child in swaddling clothes, and this causes the wounded great and extreme pain. Never, did I find myself in such a hell. . . ."

The hell continued for fifty excruciating hours. As Champlain had expected, the Onandagas and presently some of their Iroquois neighbors gave pursuit. The attackers were obliged to run for their lives all the way to Stony Point.

The anguished leader noted that his force was more effective in retreat than on attack. Mile after mile, hour after hour, they trotted through the forests. There was no thought of hunting or feasting. All night and all the following day and the day after that Champlain was borne along on the warrior's strong shoulders. Bushes and briars slapped and cut his face. Again and again his carrier forded rivers which were shoulder or head deep.

When the fleeing attackers finally recovered their hidden canoes and put them to water, Champlain had to be lifted into a canoe like a bag of pelts. Returned to Quebec Habitation he was still too lame to move. A month passed before he was able to limp from his quarters. Champlain, meanwhile, suffered with the greatest humiliation of his life. He had lost the battle. And he sensed that the loss would prove enormously costly to France.

As soon as he was able to limp along without a shoulder to lean on, Champlain determined to set forth again. Now that he had failed as a war-maker he was doubly determined to succeed as a peacemaker. His special concern at this time was in keeping the friendship of the Hurons. The proud people of the Far North had not supported the Algonquins in the unsuccessful move against the Iroquois. Would the Huron now turn against the Algonquin? Would he foresake his friendship with New France?

Champlain hoped the answers were No. But, feeble

Father le Caron set up a mission.

as he was, he resolved to set forth again for the northern country. Since the winter would soon be settling in and the northern rivers would shortly be frozen over, he resolved to move at once.

Hurons were still heading north over the more than twelve hundred miles of river route. Champlain asked permission to go along as guest of one of the canoe fleets.

The chief said, "Come ahead! You will be welcomed as before. But remember the great winter now settles, and the journey will be hard and cold."

Champlain, of course, knew this. He also knew that his wounds were far from being healed. He still limped very badly. Even so, he set out for another peace mission.

Early in January, 1616, Champlain arrived at the Huron town called Carhagouha, where Father le Caron had set up a mission. The brave Recollect welcomed his sponsor.

CHAPTER **10**

THE HOSTS OF JUBILATION

The winter was bitter cold. But to his own surprise and delight Champlain found himself growing stronger. He presently moved from the little mission house to a wigwam which was tightly sealed with mooseskins and quite comfortable. There he continued to complete maps and charts and to make journal records in prose that sparkled like a cataract of diamonds.

He told how the Hurons made delicious bread of rye flour into which they had beaten wild berries. He learned to enjoy the staple winter fare of corn and dried beans pounded together in stone mortars. He even learned to endure the partly spoiled corn-on-the-cob which the Hurons preserved by burying in soft mud.

It wasn't exactly preserved, but it was, as they said, "mellowed." The honored guest noted that the Hurons used fresh meat to keep up their generally good health throughout the long winters. Their favorite meat was young bear which they raised like barnyard livestock. In the spring the Hurons caught the young cubs and placed them in log pens. Then, as the bears grew, the Indians moved them to fattening cages and in due time changed them to steaks, chops and soup stocks.

"Quite tasty," Champlain reported.

When April opened the long trails of rivers, the voyager returned to Quebec Habitation in company of a party of Huron fur traders. He was pleased to see that women as well as men were now living in Quebec. In addition to the good wife and attractive daughters of apothecary Hebert, who had lately moved to Quebec from Port Royal, a company clerk had brought home a bride and two more married couples were en route from France. Champlain was therefore quite determined to bring his own wife to the New World. Helene was grown up by now. He was confident she could make a happy life in New France.

Once more the news in Paris was not good. One mishap was wholly unexpected. Prince de Condé was in jail charged with inciting rebellion against the Crown and stealing public monies. The arresting officer, the Marquis de Thamine, had been made Viceroy.

Champlain gained audience with young Louis XIII to

plead the cause, as he stated it, "of making the natives men, then Christians." He brought along the aging Count de Monts, who was still a principal owner of the company, or association, and as a very special witness, Father Joseph le Caron, whose homecoming Champlain had carefully arranged and kept more or less secret. Father Joseph planned to return to his Huron mission on the next outbound ship; he had come along as a very special favor to his very special friend and insisted that the Hurons must not be left indefinitely without a priest.

Both the Recollect and De Monts supported Champlain's requests for more priests, more colonists, and more generous support for a French-and-Indian colony. But the other stockholders answered loudly that their interests were in more furs, and they would not pay good money for more colonists, or soldiers, or, indeed, missionaries.

Champlain persisted in his project of persuasion. He next carried his plea to the Chamber of Commerce of Paris. The Chamber sided with Champlain and asked another audience with the King. His Majesty was more cordial this time. He recommended granting money for building a new town on the St. Lawrence; also for recruiting and equipping a party of three hundred French farmers who would serve doubly as soldiers. (Champlain found this hard to imagine.) Also young Louis XIII expressed himself in favor, as he stated it, of "establishing the Christian faith among an infinite number of souls."

Champlain was confident that the young King meant well. But he also knew that royal recommendations did not always crop out as factual matters. He was not wholly surprised when the three hundred colonists turned out to be only one butcher and one needlemaker and their respective families.

But the Viceroy's assistant was thankful for these. He was even more thankful for the two more Recollect Fathers who volunteered to serve as missionaries in the New World. He promptly assigned one as resident pastor for the Montagnais Algonquins and the other for service at the proposed interracial colony which would presently be named Montreal. As a surprise play, Champlain next moved by way of the Bishop's Council of Paris to gain the Pope's permission to hold at Quebec the New World's first religious jubilee.

The next venture in persuasion was not successful. When Champlain suggested again to his young wife that she was now quite grown up and would find living in New France most interesting, Helene seemed disturbed and frightened. She insisted she was not yet ready for the "great change." In one more year she believed she would be. Champlain's deep disappointment was soothed somewhat by his young brother-in-law. Young Eustache Boullé, then fifteen, asked if he might go to New France.

"Come ahead!" Champlain replied. "I only wish your interest in New France were more contagious."

Eustache's father, Nicholas Boullé, addressed his son-in-law who was eight years older than he. "Samuel, I count on you to look after your brother-in-law and have him back here within a year. Eustache is only a boy."

"He appears to me like a real man," Champlain answered. "I expect he will like the other fine youths he will meet in our habitations. But I will be back in less than a year. I suggest we let your son decide for himself what he wishes to do then." He added easily, "I somehow have the feeling Eustache will soon find himself quite fond of what you call the 'wilderness for savages.'"

A few days later Champlain boarded ship, having first made certain that the two young priests, the butcher, and the needlemaker and the families of the two latter were comfortable aboard. Champlain once more took over as pilot of the *Don de Dieu*. At his side was young Eustache who was eager to learn about the strange and beautiful science of navigation.

"You can be my lieutenant," Champlain told him. "As of now, I myself am not even a lieutenant."

"What are you then?" the youth enquired.

Champlain smiled feebly. "I am listed as 'Royal Explorer of New France.' In order to remedy that I may have to appoint myself Royalty Explorer of Old France."

By the following September, the self-appointed Royalty Explorer of Old France was again in Paris on a self-directed mission.

"This time you are going home with me to New France," he told his wife.

"Where is our Eustache?" Helene asked.

" 'Our Eustache' will be waiting our arrival in Quebec. He likes New France so well he vows he never wishes to see or smell Paris again."

"What a strange boy!" the Boullés chorused.

"I see him as a future great man," Champlain answered.

For the next few weeks Champlain kept extremely busy. Within a few more weeks Paris stationers and bookstalls were showing another new Champlain book— *Voyages and Discoveries Made in New France, 1615–1618*, by Sieur de Champlain, Captain Ordinaire for the King in the Western Hemisphere.

It was the weakest of Champlain's books, and, according to some contemporaries, it did not sell very well. But at least the young King Louis XIII read it. Long before the winter was ended, Champlain found himself with a royal commission as Governor of New France— "officially empowered to appoint officers, attend defenses, and otherwise serve as baron (caretaker) for His Royal Majesty of France."

"How does it feel to be the Governor's Lady?" Champlain asked his wife.

Helene was not quite sure. She granted that she was now a full-grown woman, but, even so, the wilderness teeming with savages seemed rather terrifying. At least for the first few months she would wish to take along some friends—ladies-in-waiting.

April and sailing time found the newly elevated Governor of New France aboard ship. This time Helene was at his side, and at hers were three of her young women friends. Fathers Jarnet and de Baillif, both of the Recollect Friars, were the new missionary team. Other homeland members of the ship's company included two bulls and two cows and a pair of donkeys which Champlain brought along to better the livestock resources of New France. The cattle mooed occasionally; the donkeys brayed frequently.

Apparently the passengers didn't mind too much. But when the donkeys were first resettled at the Quebec Habitation, visiting Indians heard their brays and, believing they were Indian-devouring demons, ran like the very wind.

At Tadoussac, young Eustache Boullé waited to greet the long delayed couple. Grown taller and stronger, the youth had canoed downriver alone. Champlain was so favorably impressed that he promptly and officially named his young brother-in-law Governor's Aide.

The return to Quebec Habitation was something short of being delightful. Brother Pacifique had lately become the first of the missionaries to give his life in line of duty. Apothecary Louis Hebert's eldest daughter, Mrs. Jacques Jonquest, who had been the first Catholic bride in New France, had recently died in childbirth. The Quebec Habitation was badly run down. Its sheds and houses had not been cared for and most of the roofs had began to leak. Nothing appeared to be well kept and correct except the Heberts' ten-acre farm. It was one beautiful garden of vegetables, fruit trees, flowers, herbs, and grain plots.

Champlain celebrated homecoming by walking with

his wife to the little chapel where the couple gave thanks for a safe arrival. Then the Governor undertook a swarm of new works. He planned and directed building a log fort directly above the habitation. At the same time he put in action plans for another fur trading post located at Three Rivers, about halfway between Montreal and Quebec. He then began active work for an Indian trading fair at Montreal and another religious jubilee at Quebec.

The fur trade was improving, but the Governor's home life was not. In August, when her ladies-in-waiting returned to Paris, Helene was again quite lonely. Both her husband and her brother were usually away. Though the Heberts treated her most graciously, Helene found little of common interest with the wives of the butcher or the needlemaker. She longed for the pleasantries of the Paris she knew and loved. And she was appalled by finding herself made a kind of goddess by the unending streams of visiting Indians.

Champlain plead for patience. "You will like the wilderness and its people ever so much better when you know them better," he assured his pretty young wife. "Any day now the supply ship will be arriving. . . ."

"I'm quite sure it won't bring the things I wish most," Helene sighed. "Like parfaits and chocolates and sweet custard pastries. . . ."

Champlain had to agree on those points, but he promised that the ship would bring her new gowns direct from Paris, and fine cheeses and wines, and bolts of ribbon and laces, and perhaps even a new chair. "And it will bring us more money," he added. "I have a salary raise, you know."

"I understood your salary is a hundred crowns a year," she said.

"That was back when I was only the royal geographer," Champlain hurried to explain. "As Governor I am going to be paid two hundred crowns a year. And that is as much as we truly need."

"Father's store makes more than that in one day," Helene noted.

When the next supply ship arrived it brought all the pleasant things Champlain had promised and for good measure about twenty new colonists and ten cows. The ship also brought word that Admiral Montmorency, Commander of the Royal Navy of France, had been appointed Viceroy of New France. Champlain was again named Governor of New France. As promised, his salary was now two hundred crowns a year.

"If you saved all your pay for five years, you would have money enough to buy a fairly good horse," Helene pointed out.

"I like cows better," the Governor answered. No doubt he was thinking of the needs of New France. He might also have recalled his sad adventure with the falling horse on the great Western Highway to Paris.

But there was work to do. Quebec had grown to be a "large" settlement with sixty French residents. It was currently the scene of two events which Champlain marked as historic. One of these was the birth of the first Frenchman in the New World—Baby Abraham, the son of the ship's pilot and Marguerite Langlois-Martin. The other event was the marriage of Guillemette, apothecary Hebert's younger daughter, to French-born G. Couillard.

Returning to his role as peacemaker, Champlain persuaded several Iroquois tribes to send peace emissaries whom he entertained royally at the Quebec Habitation. Next he sponsored what he called a festival of good will. This brought together more than a hundred chiefs representing almost as many tribes or settlements of Iroquois, Algonquins, and Hurons. As another "first," and in keeping with his newly granted authority as Governor of New France, Champlain commissioned a Montagnais Algonquin chief as "Captain Ordinaire de France." In return, the Montagnais agreed to establish farms and forever keep the peace with France and his neighbors.

During the summer of 1623, with the arrival of Brother Gabriel Sagard, Champlain gave his blessings and help to setting up a mission in the Huron country. Etienne Brulé and eleven colonists volunteered to help set up the new outpost of faith.

Early the following year the hard-working Governor made plans for and changed to successful fact the great peace parley of 1624. The event took place late in May. It began with a tremendous feast for thirty-five canoe-loads of chiefs. The party closed with a declaration of lasting peace between all Iroquois, Algonquins, and Hurons.

Helene was homesick for Paris.

By his own admission, Champlain was the happiest of Frenchmen, new or old. He admitted that he was not especially new. He was now fifty-six. His wife, Helene, though beautiful and twenty-five, did not claim to be the happiest woman in New France. After four years of her New World adventure, Helene Champlain was still homesick for Paris. Late in August, 1624, the couple went back to Paris, Samuel for a turn of what he called "sail mending." Sadly, his wife went home to stay.

Champlain found himself with another new commander. Viceroy and Admiral Duc de Montmorency vowed that even as an armchair viceroy he was obliged to do more work and worry for New France than for the French Navy. So he had sold his viceroyalty to his nephew, Duc de Ventadour.

Champlain formed an instant friendship with young Ventadour whom he found to be deeply religious and strongly in favor of more churches and missions for New France. His first official act as viceroy was to grant money for sending six Jesuit missionaries to New France. The group included such revered names as Fathers Charles Lalemant, Ennemond Masse and the soon-to-be-martyred Father Jean Brébeuf. After five years in the office Ventadour resigned to enter the priesthood.

Champlain found himself with another and less resounding title: "Lieutenant for New France." The new Viceroy directed that he spend a year in Paris helping reorganize the sponsoring company, by now finally named the Hundred Associates. The task was difficult.

Stockholders continued to feud and obstruct. They continued to insist that they desired more furs, fewer missionaries, and less expensive colonies.

When the six Jesuits arrived at Tadoussac on the headwaters of the St. Lawrence, they found that the quartermaster had been instructed not to permit them to disembark. At that point four of the Recollect Fathers joined in spiriting the Jesuits off the ship and upriver to the little chapel near Quebec. Almost instantly the Jesuits began building Notre Dame des Agnes, which became one of the great mission churches of the New World.

Helene Champlain was now living in her parents' home to wait the next Paris visit of her husband. On returning to New France, Champlain chose as official aides Father Joseph le Caron, whom he named as spiritual adviser, and his young brother-in-law, Eustache Boullé, who now had the rather odd title of "lieutenant for the Lieutenant."

Champlain lost another dear companion by the death of his longtime friend and most valuable helper, Louis Hebert, the apothecary, who passed away on the Day of St. Paul's Conversion, January 25. Champlain recorded the gentle Louis' last words:

"I die happy since it has pleased the Lord to do me the grace of seeing savages converted . . . I beg you to love them (the Indians) as I have and assist them according to your powers."

Within hours after the pharmacist had been buried, Champlain was busily fulfilling his friend's request. He tramped on snowshoes to the headwaters of the Richelieu River to make peaceful settlement of a very dangerous quarrel. Without permission of their chiefs, a band of young Algonquin warriors had captured a party of visiting Iroquois. Champlain persuaded the young hotheads to release their prisoners. This almost certainly quelled what could have been a ruinous war between the two Indian federations.

The following winter, Champlain's sixtieth, was one of dark troubles. It followed a summer of prolonged drought and skimpy crops. Particularly in the eastern country, Acadia, the Indians were not able to harvest any crops at all. To make matters worse many of their fishing streams ran dry and most of the game animals vanished from the grasslands and woods.

As winter began, great throngs of the hungry people, including thousands of the Montagnais Algonquins, began moving into the St. Lawrence Valley in the frantic hope of finding food. Champlain shared the colony food stores as generously as he dared, but there was nowhere near enough food to give. By the end of November, the leader was obliged to place all colonists, then numbering about three hundred, on severe rations of flour and grain.

On an early December evening while Champlain was dining alone, he heard a faltering knock on the door of his headquarters cabin. He answered the door to find there three little Indian girls. Their drawn faces, bulging eyes, and unnatural leanness were among the telltale signs of prolonged hunger. As well as he could guess, the eldest of the three was about fourteen, the second about twelve, and the youngest only eight or nine. Quite certain that the three unspeaking callers had come to beg food, only to find themselves still too proud to beg, Champlain motioned the children to come in and warm themselves before the big fireplace. When they had done this, he divided his waiting supper into three parts, brought extra bread and cheese from the fireplace cupboard, and invited the girls to have dinner. While they ate like starved animals, Champlain eyed them thoughtfully.

The beadwork on their tunic dresses indicated they were Montagnais Algonquins, also that they were sisters. Since Champlain still had considerable difficulty speaking Algonquin, he took a brief leave and returned with his young brother-in-law, by now a very skillful linguist.

Eustache questioned and translated: "They are sisters. They don't appear to have any clan or family name. They say their mother died recently. Their father and older brothers set out to the great northern country about a month ago in hopes of taking a moose in the deep snow. Four days ago the little girls set out to find their missing kin. They got lost, and here they are."

"And their names?" Champlain asked.

Eustache shook his head. "I doubt if I can say them correctly."

"Never mind trying," Champlain said. "We'll just name them Faith, Hope and Charity. And we will take them in," he added.

"But, sir . . ."

"Just call me Brother Samuel . . . I've never been blessed with a daughter. So now I'm adopting three."

"How?" Eustache asked.

"Very simply," his famous brother-in-law answered. "I'll just take them in here. I'll ask Madames Hebert and Coulliard to make them some warm dresses out of the black suits I keep for my Paris trips . . . I don't plan any more Paris trips right away. I've enough rations to feed these young ladies. After all I never wanted to be a fat man. They can live in this cabin."

"But where will you lodge, Brother Samuel?"

"With you, Brother Eustache. I'm moving in tonight. Aren't you glad? Tomorrow we'll build a partition in this cabin so my daughters may have a room of their own."

The winter seemed to fade quickly into another spring. Champlain was delighted with his three adopted daughters and they with him. Madame Hebert became their godmother and caretaker.

Then, on a day in early May, he faced some less happy developments. While he was directing springtime cleaning and repair of the habitation grounds and some of the buildings, two Frenchmen arrived at the log-built pier, beached their canoe, and came scurrying toward the swarthy-skinned leader whose hair was by now snow white. Champlain recognized the two herdsmen he had lately stationed at the newly opened cattle ranch on a great prairie far downriver. The habitans reported that six strange ships, all heavily armed and manned by British crews, were waiting off Tadoussac, the supply base.

"They are war craft," the excited herdsmen declared. "They have been sent to destroy the cattle and take over the colony. They are already blockading the river's mouth."

Champlain listened with concern. He had already heard rumors by the grapevine that France and England were again at the verge of war. He had received no official notice of this. But he reasoned that the strange ships might very well be British blockaders. If they were, no official message from France could have gotten through.

The leader called a meeting of family heads and asked for volunteers to travel downriver and find out the facts. Six followers volunteered; his young brother-in-law was the very first.

"Dress yourselves like Indians," Champlain directed. "Look over the ships and get back here as soon as possible. The rest of us will be setting up defenses. . . ."

Before his scouting party was out of sight, Champlain began the work of counting all supplies. All food stores were at a dangerous low; if the report were true, severe rationing would be the only alternative to starvation. During the long winter the hunters had used up most of the supply of gunpowder. Only one fifty-pound keg remained—barely enough to fire the habitation's one cannon one time. If the strange craft really were British no more French supplies could be expected.

The next day Champlain learned that the herdsmen had indeed reported truthfully. The ships were not only British, they were alertly British. When the scouts dressed like Indians had tried to look too closely, four of the six, including Eustache Boullé, had been captured. One had escaped, but the leader's brother-in-law was still a prisoner.

"They are privateers," the scouts explained. "They aren't the regular navy. But they fly British war banners."

He had barely heard the report when Champlain saw another canoe come skimming into the river landing. A young man in blue raised a white flag and trotted toward him. The stranger saluted and handed Champlain a letter written in French. The letter was signed, "Your Affectionate Servant, David Kirke."

More than vaguely Champlain recognized the name. David Kirke was the eldest of five sons of Gervase Kirke, a French-English ship merchant of Dieppe and one of Champlain's longtime friends. But clearly David and his brothers had changed their country. David commanded the British ships and his brothers were captains. They represented the British crown as British chartered privateers. As such, they had already blockaded the great river and they demanded Champlain's immediate surrender. Otherwise they planned to forceably seize the French colonies, stored supplies and cattle. Pending such

action they proposed to starve the habitations into sub-
mission.

Champlain answered tersely: "We will not surrender. With due help of God, our Indian allies, and our
home forces, New France will defend herself."

The Kirke messenger had little more than boarded
his canoe and set out downriver when two more of
Champlain's scouts arrived. They had managed to break
free of their captors. They had also managed to pick up
some important news from the French ship men at Tadoussac.

Cardinal de Richelieu was the new French premier.
The Cardinal was supporting New France, its colonies,
and churches. He had lately reorganized the Hundred
Associates to include government leaders as well as merchants. The Cardinal had promised to supply three
more priests for each settlement and had enacted the
Hundred Associates' promise to settle two hundred
families in New France each year and to support them
for three years. The Hundred Associates had also lately
sent four supply ships.

"The news is inspiring," Champlain agreed. "But if
this blockade holds it cannot help us."

He shortly heard that the four supply ships had
reached Tadoussac. The Kirke flotilla had captured
three of them and the fourth had managed to head back
to France.

Champlain began making ready for a long siege. Food
supplies permitted each family head only a weekly
handout of half-a-pound each of corn, peas and barley.

He took out the colony's store of beaver skin and began trading these with the inland Indians for meat or any other food they had—including smoked eel. He dispatched fishing and hunting parties and sent out the other colonists to gather edible roots, herbs, wild fruits and berries, and other wild growing foodstuffs. Faith, Hope and Charity turned out to be among the most able of the root and herb pickers. One of the Jesuits, Father Nouc, proved to be the grand champion fisherman. Huron friends were able to bring in a few canoe loads of grain from the Far North.

Life in the besieged colonies went on. One day in June, the eldest of Champlain's adopted daughters, Faith, asked permission to go back to her tribe and family. She had heard that her father and brothers were at last returned from the northern country. She thanked the Great Chief Whitehair for his many kindnesses, but begged to go back to her people.

Champlain granted her wish and arranged with Montagnais friends to see the girl safely home. "Her life is her own," the troubled foster father said. He hoped the two younger sisters would choose to stay on. They were very happy to do so. The food was getting rather bad but Hope and Charity insisted that their "adopted father" was indeed very good.

Then, on an otherwise lovely July day, the brothers Kirke closed in.

"I was alone at the fort," Champlain wrote. "Some of my companions had gone to fish, others to look for edible roots. . . . The two little native girls had gone with them. . . ."

Then, about mid-morning, one of the root pickers ran out to the little fort to report that three British ships were in view.

"Make ready to defend," Champlain ordered.

He saw both Jesuit and Recollect Fathers hurrying to join the defense force which the leader was rapidly stationing. He next saw the invading privateers. The first was a flagship with ten cannon showing; the other two were smaller cutters, each mounting six guns. The first ship hoisted a white flag to request interview. A young officer came ashore in a dory and handed Champlain a note demanding that he surrender. It was signed, "Your Very Affectionate Servants, Louis and Thomas Kirke."

The messenger did not speak French, and Champlain did not speak English. Jesuit Father de la Roche delivered Champlain's answer in Latin which the British messenger understood.

The answer was a masterpiece of dignity and candor. Anyone could see that Quebec could not stand off the powerfully armed invaders. Champlain did not deny this. He began his answer with a firm warning that the flotilla was not to attempt a landing until all terms were agreed to. He next demanded that the British flotilla assure a safe return of all the colonists who wished to return, including himself and his adopted daughters.

The officer promptly reported the Kirkes' answer. They were willing to guarantee a safe return to France for all French citizens requesting it. They would assure the safety of all personal property, all church properties and pelts or furs owned by the colonists. They would not grant passage to the little Indian girls whom they could not list as "nationals." They would, however, promise safe residence to all or any colonists who chose to remain with Louis Kirke who would be the British-authorized commander of the French settlements.

Champlain knew he had no choice other than to yield. His people were on the verge of starvation. They had nothing to use except bows and arrows against the deadly British guns. But the leader took time to make a vow to all present that if God in His wisdom would return the settlements to France, Champlain would return to Quebec and there build and dedicate a Church of Our Lady of Recovery—Notre Dame de Recouvrance.

He then asked for an audience with Captain Louis Kirke.

"The two young native girls are my rightfully adopted daughters," he explained. "I stand responsible for their upbringing and would therefore take them back to France with me."

"Sorry, Excellency," Kirke answered. "My orders are fixed. They are not my personal choice."

"I will guarantee proper support of my daughters. I have sufficient funds in furs, nearly a thousand pelts easily worth a livre each."

"You will require all that for your own use, Excellency. Living in France has grown costly," the young captain pointed out.

"Feel no concern for me," Champlain replied. "I have been without money many times before. But these children are my responsibility in the sight of God."

Madame Hebert moved forward to address Champlain. "Liege, my daughter and son-in-law and I will be happy and honored to keep the little girls while you are away. We have all faith that New France will again be free and you will again be its leader."

Champlain thanked his longtime friend. Needlemaker Nicette stepped forward. "Your dear ones will also have good neighbors. Six families of us have agreed to stay on in Quebec to wait your return."

Champlain thanked them all, then kissed his adopted daughters good-bye. All three wept as they parted. The leader's sorrow was somewhat lessened when he found that his brother-in-law was in safe custody and would also be taken back to France.

On October 20, the captor ship pulled into an English harbor, Plymouth. There all aboard learned of a truce between England and France many weeks before the capture of Quebec. Britain's admiralty had failed to inform the Kirkes of this. They were now ordered to discharge their captives and provide them passage to France.

But Champlain went directly to London to the French embassy there to ask prompt return of the habitations to their rightful owners. He sailed from London to Paris where Cardinal Richelieu advised him that England's king granted that the actions of the Kirkes were unlawful and that British claims on New France would be withdrawn.

Throughout France churches were supporting the colonies with prayer. The Jesuits instituted a special daily Mass; the Ursuline Sisters, a perpetual prayer for the restoration of New France. On March 29, 1632, the prayers were answered. "By God's will and the Treaty of Germain-en-large," Champlain explained.

Now that April had come and Champlain was officially named "In Charge of Operations for New France," the first citizen of that great land waited at Honfleur to sail west again. He was then sixty-four and, as he stated, his hair was whiter than last February's snow.

But Champlain was a happy man. Prayers had been answered. New France was free again. As he boarded the *Don de Dieu* in company with his loyal lieutenant Eustache Boullé, the grand old man of New France confided that from the western sky he heard what he chose to term the angel hosts of jubilation.

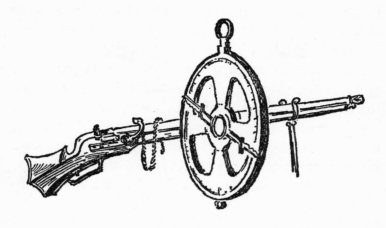

CHAPTER **11**

A SAFE PLACE TO SLEEP

As Premier of France, Cardinal de Richelieu was taking a very unusual stand regarding New France. He was keeping his promises.

Champlain had sailed with a group of seven new missionaries. Before they were across the Atlantic, the good ship *Le Caen* was also en route with two hundred colonists St. Lawrence bound. The list included soldiers from the Royal Army, carpenters, masons, blacksmiths, woodsmen, and more than a hundred farmers. Long before garden planting time, the new settlers were busily at work restoring the habitations. The Kirke brothers had done a very bad job of maintaining the settlement. But now there were plenty of hands to repair leaky roofs and clear new fields and garden sites.

On arrival at the supply base Champlain found a most welcome packet addressed to him and delivered by a French warship. It was his renewed commission as Governor of New France. Also waiting his return were generous supplies of flour, gunpowder, cloth, leather, farming tools, axes, and a tremendous store of knives and other trader goods to barter for furs. Also waiting was a pigmy fleet of shiny new sail-and-oar boats for use on the St. Lawrence.

The restored Governor arrived at Quebec in a mood of thanksgiving. He showed it by directing and helping prepare a great public dinner of bear meat to which he invited all the colonists and hundreds of Indians.

When he called at the Couillard home Champlain learned that his adopted daughters, Hope and Charity, had gone back to their family and tribe. They had gone happily and of their own free will. They would return from time to time to visit their Father Samuel. They asked that when his work permitted he come and visit them.

Champlain presently accepted the invitation. But for several weeks he was almost unbelievably busy. While the newcomers built cabins and planted gardens, the Governor summoned his new force of masons and carpenters and rebuilt the little fort. There he stationed his token army of fourteen French regulars, handsomely uniformed and fully armed with pikes, muskets,

Project followed project with almost dizzying speed.

powder and lead. He was determined that his beloved habitation would not again be open to easy capture.

Next he began to organize a force of Indian allies numbering in all about three thousand men. It was not the usual kind of an army or battle party. Rather, it was a force organized to improve and expand the fur trade, improve and develop Indian farming methods, and "advance the practice of religion."

"The enterprise is wholly honorable," Champlain assured his Cardinal and the King's Council; "it is all for the glory of God. . . ." Project followed project with almost dizzying speed. As soon as crops were planted all the colonists joined their leader in completing the Church of Our Lady of Recovery.

Then the Governor of New France issued his first official order. It prohibited the selling, trading or giving of intoxicating liquor to any Indians. After more than three and a third centuries the substance of this order remains Canadian law and is widely in force throughout the United States.

Champlain next directed rebuilding the fur trading post and fort at the Three Rivers. Then boldly he opened all trading posts to all Indians who cared to use them, quite regardless of tribe or federation or brotherhood. More and more of the native fur traders began appearing. Canoes laden with furs came sweeping in from all directions. Along with fine furs, they brought fine friendships and the brightening hope for peace.

The smallish, dark-complexioned man with snow-white hair found himself much more than governor of the largest colony beyond the Western Ocean or, at that time, in the entire world. On both sides of the Atlantic, Champlain had grown to be a symbol of the cause of good will and fellowship among neighbors and nations. Throughout more than a million square miles of the continent which some were beginning to call North America, the name Champlain had grown to mean "friend of the Indian."

His colonists, too, were helping shape an enlarged image of their leader. They were beginning to see him as more than just their helper in what had been apparently unending troubles and distress. The New World Frenchmen were no longer year around victims of hunger, poverty and privation. Now even the newcomers were growing good crops in fertile lands and living in houses which were comfortable, even if humble. They were beginning to own livestock, at least a few cattle, sheep, and pigs. They were learning how to hunt and fish and how to trap and trade furs. They now had churches and chapels, and they would very soon have schools for their children.

As he grew older Champlain paid more heed to food and the pleasures of good dining. He encouraged his people to hunt and fish and make the best uses of their catches. He challenged everyone to join in a neighborly contest to see who could grow the best vegetable garden. Though many, including the priests, insisted that the Governor himself was the best gardener in New France, Champlain made certain that he never won the prize.

He found time to locate and harvest the various native fruits, particularly plums, blueberries, raspberries, and wild cherries. Recalling that prunes, or dried plums, were his favorite sweet as a child, Champlain encouraged his people to pick the delicious wild fruits and berries and to dry them for winter use. While urging and showing ways to improve the home-grown fare, the Governor imported a few of the grand old standbys of French cookery, particularly cheeses, cured bacon, and olive oil. Champlain also gave greater attention to what he termed the "condiments of a good fare."

In the big commissary room where all the company assembled for the evening meal, Champlain sat at the big table. The colonists and Indian guests took turns at the Governor's table. "This great table," Champlain noted, "is the crib and cradle for the New World."

In 1634, at a very alert and busy sixty-six, Champlain once more journeyed back to Paris to put finishing touches on his fourth and final book which he entitled simply *Voyages*.

When the book was published and various official errands attended, Champlain sailed again for New France. He arrived in Quebec in time to spend the Christmas which was his sixty-seventh birthday. Once more he was welcomed by his colonists and the endlessly growing throngs of his Indian friends. Once more he spoke briefly and with sincere warmth. One sentence lingered in the minds of several listeners, including Father le Jeune's: "The advice I would give all adventurers is to seek a place where they may sleep in safety."

As time was soon to tell, Champlain had again followed his own advice. During the following October the great builder of New France suffered a cerebral stroke. He was working in his garden at the time. Neighbors ran to him and found him prostrate and unable to speak or move.

They carried him to his newly built cottage on a forested ridge overlooking the great St. Lawrence. There, for three weeks, the stricken man lay motionless and unable to speak. But he smiled a great deal, and hour after hour he looked out the big window. He could see the passing river traffic. But he seemed most interested in viewing the woodlands, first in gaily colored autumn garments, then in the soft graying imagery of bare trunks and limbs, and finally in the piling white snows.

When Father le Caron suggested that it might be well to write down his will, Champlain managed to point to a bit of paper beside his pillow. His shaky handwriting recorded simply: "I nominate the Virgin Mary my heir."

As the St. Lawrence began to freeze over, Champlain recovered his power to speak. When this became known, more and more colonists, priests, and Indians came to visit. The bedridden old man welcomed each one as his own son or daughter.

"Old Champlain is still not walking or waving his arms," he conceded, "but just wait until spring comes. I'll be out planting gardens with the best of you, and if you are not very careful, I will be besting you."

In the presence of his confessor, Father le Caron,

Champlain wrote out what he termed his last testament of things earthly. His entire worldly wealth consisted of ten shares in the colonizing company, the Hundred Associates, and about six hundred beaver skins, then valued at about nine hundred livres, or somewhere near eleven hundred dollars. He directed that the total be given to his beloved Church of Our Lady of Recovery. He did not know, of course, that within a short while his will would be contested.

The contesting party was a certain Marie Hersaut, once of Brouage, who claimed to be Champlain's cousin and his only surviving blood kin. Mme. Hersaut claimed that Cousin Samuel's will violated the terms of his wedding contract.

Helene Champlain and her family, the Boullés, made no such claim. Her brother Eustache remained loyally with his leader, and the two talked together of spiritual things.

"I can never be as great or as a devout a Christian as you are, Brother Samuel," Eustache said. "But in my smaller and less splendid way, I will try."

The following year Eustache Boullé returned to Paris and began study for the priesthood. After ten years in novitiates and monasteries, he became a Minimite Monk. His sister and Champlain's wife, Helene, was already shaping plans to enter an Ursuline convent in Paris.

Samuel Champlain continued to speak of the present. With great reverence, Father le Jeune wrote for *The Record of Jesuits:* "He (Champlain) crowned his virtues with sentiments of feelings so lofty that he astonished us all. . . ."

The Governor of New France was not too ill to make and direct plans for celebration of Christmas which would also be his sixty-eighth birthday. He instructed his brother-in-law and aide to make arrangements for a Christmas Day dinner for all the habitation and all visiting friends, including particularly the priests, missionaries, and Indians.

"See that all are fed well. Let each of the fathers take part in leading prayers, and let all join in singing happy songs."

"Of faith or cheer?" Eustache asked.

"Both, they are truly the same . . . And open the great day by firing the big fort cannon," he added. "Both the morning gun and scripture reading must herald the grand day. Remember it is my birthday only incidentally . . . We will celebrate only the birthday of the Son of Man."

The Governor's plans were carried out in every detail. Father le Jeune recorded how a "cavalcade of friends," including priests, chiefs, and habitans carried their leader to his beloved Notre Dame de Recouvrance for celebration of the midnight High Mass.

But Champlain did not hear the morning gun. Before the dawn of his sixty-eighth birthday, the great builder of New France died. He had found a place to sleep in safety.

Father Lalemant was chosen to carry the news back

to Paris and to inform the widow. Helene Champlain was accepted and completed plans for becoming a novice in the Ursulines. Thirteen years later she bequeathed her total of wedding dowry and all other possessions to the founding of an Order of Meaux convent.

Cousin Marie, meanwhile, had received on court decree Champlain's shares in the Hundred Associates. But the rest of his tiny estate was given to his beloved Notre Dame de Recouvrance where colonists, Indians, priests, and missionaries shortly joined in building and consecrating *La Chapelle de M. de Champlain*.

In worldly goods, Samuel Champlain had died as he had lived, a poor man. In deed and spirit, he was immeasurably rich. For he was the great builder of New France, a keeper of the faith, and discoverer and shaper of a wonderful land which would live and live and never die.

FOR MORE ABOUT SAMUEL DE CHAMPLAIN

Bigger, H. P. (ed.). *The Works of Samuel de Champlain*, 1604–1632. Reprinted, translated and annotated by six Canadian scholars. Vol. 1, 1604–7, translated by W. F. Ganary; vol. 2, 1608–13, translated by John Squaer; vol. 3, 1615–18, translated and edited by H. H. Langston; vol. 4, 1608–20, translated by H. H. Langston; vol. 5, 1620–29, translated by W. D. LeSeuer; vol. 6, 1629–32, translated by W. D. LeSeuer and H. H. Langston. Toronto: The Champlain Society, 1922–1936.

Bishop, Morris. *Champlain, the Life of Fortitude*. New York: Alfred A. Knopf, Inc., 1948.

Dex, Edwin Asa. *Champlain*. New York: D. Appleton Co., 1903.

MacBeath, George. *Champlain and the St. John*. Saint John, Canada: New Brunswick Historical Society, 1954.

INDEX

Faith, 162–164, 168
Fontainebleau, 109, 119, 121

Hebert, Guillemette, *see* Couillard, Guillemette
Hebert, Louis, 80, 85, 87–88, 93, 150, 155–156, 158, 161
Hebert, Madame, 88, 93, 150, 155–156, 164, 171
Henry IV, King of France (*also* called Henry of Navarre), 13, 20–22, 31, 41–43, 46, 89–90, 92–93, 109–113
Hersaut, Marie, 180, 182
Holland, 30, 75, 130
Honfleur, 30, 114, 172
Hope, 162–164, 168–171, 174
Hudson, Henry, 75, 108–110
Hudson River, 38, 75–76, 105, 138
Huguenots, 14, 18
Huronia, 115–116, 127, 134, 137
Huron Indians, 34, 38, 92, 101–104, 111–112, 115–117, 127–128, 132–133, 135–139, 146, 148–151, 158

Iroquois Indians, 34–35, 38, 40, 101, 103, 105–106, 108, 132–133, 136–146, 158, 162
Iroquet, 138, 141

Jamestown, 75
Jamet, Father Denis, 131–133
Jarnet, Father, 154
Jesuits, 25–26, 90–91, 93, 95, 160–161, 168–169, 172, 181
Jonas, 80–81, 88–90
Jonquest, Mrs. Jacques, 88, 93, 150, 155

Kennebunkport, 65
Kirke, David, 166, 168–173
Kirke, Gervase, 166
Kirke, Louis, 166, 168–173
Kirke, Thomas, 166, 168–173

Lac Deschenes, 128
Lachine Rapids, 38, 116–117
Lake Champlain, 104
Lake Erie, 38
Lake George, 105
Lake Huron, 38, 134
Lake Nipissing, 134
Lake Ontario, 38, 139
Lalemant, Father Charles, 160, 181
La Roche, Father de, 169
La Rochelle, 14, 18–19, 47, 119
Le Caron, Father Joseph, 131–135, 148, 151, 161, 179
Le Jeune, Father, 178, 180–181
Louis XIII, King of France, 42, 112–113, 127, 130–131, 150–154

Maine, 16, 34, 65
Manhattan Indians, 75–76, 84, 108
Manhattan Island, 108–109
Margarita Island, 26
Marsolet, Nicholas, 99–100
Martha's Vineyard, 84
Massachusetts Bay, 65
Massachusetts Indians, 65
Masse, Father Ennemond, 160
Medici, Marie de, Queen of France, 90–91, 112, 119–122
Mexico, 22–23, 26, 28
Montagnais Indians, *see* Algonquin Indians

THE AUTHOR AND HIS BOOK

CHARLES MORROW WILSON *was born in Fayetteville, Arkansas, and received his Bachelor of Arts degree from the University of Arkansas. He also attended Christ Church College at Oxford University. A writer and economic consultant who specializes in the history of North and South America, Mr. Wilson received a "Special Citation for Distinguished Contributions to Inter-American Relations" from the University of Florida in 1960 and the "Friends of the Americas" citation from the National University of Guatemala in 1941. He was formerly a reporter for the* New York Times *and a writer for* Reader's Digest. *In addition to three novels, he has written eighteen non-fiction books, including* Meriwether Lewis of Lewis & Clark, (*Thomas Y. Crowell Co., 1933*), Ambassadors in White (*Holt, Rinehart & Winston, Inc., 1944*), *and* Common Sense Credit (*Devin-Adair Co., 1962*). *For this book, Mr. Wilson had access to the latest Canadian research on Champlain.*

WILDERNESS EXPLORER (*Hawthorn, 1963*) *was designed by Stefan Salter and completely manufactured by*

American Book–Stratford Press. The body type is Lino-type Janson, based on the letters of Anton Janson, a Dutch punchcutter who worked between 1660 and 1687.

A HAWTHORN BOOK

Published with ecclesiastical approbation.

CREDO
BOOKS

ABOUT CREDO BOOKS

CREDO BOOKS is an important new series of biographies that will appeal to both boys and girls. The subjects of these biographies are Catholics, but their stories are not of their faith so much as how that faith helped them to lead remarkable lives. Past and present will be represented here: a sculptor who left a priceless treasure of art to mankind, or a movie star who was an idol to young and old alike; the president of a South American country who fought against and lost his life to Communist terrorists. Heroes are made by the greatness of the human spirit and all the figures to be portrayed in CREDO BOOKS were great in spirit, courage and effort, no matter what task they took upon themselves.

The authors of these new books have been carefully chosen both for their ability to make biography come alive for young people and their knowledge of their subjects. Such authors as Terry Morris, Albert Orbaan, Donald Demarest, Gary Webster, Ruth Hume, Frank Kolars and Jack Steffan will be represented.

To give CREDO BOOKS the benefit of their knowledge and experience, an editorial board of distinguished representatives from the fields of education, librarianship and the Catholic Press, as well as Hawthorn's own editorial staff, choose both subject and author for each book in the series.

As an example of the variety of personalities in this new series, you will find the following figures portrayed.

Operation Escape: The Adventure of Father O'Flaherty, by Daniel Madden

To Far Places: The Story of Francis X. Ford, by Eva K. Betz

The Lion of Poland: The Story of Paderewski, by Ruth and Paul Hume

The Conscience of a King: The Story of Thomas More, by Margaret Stanley-Wrench

Pen and Bayonet: The Story of Joyce Kilmer, by Norah Smaridge

The Man Who Found Out Why: The Story of Gregor Mendel, by Gary Webster

The Tall American: The Story of Gary Cooper, by Richard Gehman

Wings of an Eagle: The Story of Michelangelo, by Anne M. Peck with Frank and Dorothy Getlein

The Door of Hope: The Story of Katharine Drexel, by Katherine Burton

Fire of Freedom: The Story of Col. Carlos Castillo Armas, by Jack Steffan

Doctor America: The Story of Tom Dooley, by Terry Morris

The Sea Tiger: The Story of Pedro Menéndez, by Frank Kolars

The First Californian: The Story of Fray Junípero Serra, by Donald Demarest